Important Instruction

Students, Parents, and Teachers can use the URL or QR code provided below to access two full-length Lumos STAAR practice tests. Please note that these assessments are provided in the Online format only.

URL	QR Code
Visit the URL below and place the book access code **http://www.lumoslearning.com/a/tedbooks** **Access Code: G6ESTAAR-95081-P**	

Developed by Expert Teachers

Texas State Test Prep: Grade 6 English Language Arts Literacy (ELA) Practice Workbook and Full-length Online Assessments: STAAR Study Guide

Contributing Editor   -   **Heather Dorey**
Contributing Editor   -   **Janet Redell**
Contributing Editor   -   **George Smith**
Executive Producer   -   **Mukunda Krishnaswamy**
Designer and Illustrator -   **Sowmya R.**

ISBN-13: 978-1-949855-35-7

Printed in the United States of America

For permissions and additional information contact us

Lumos Information Services, LLC
PO Box 1575, Piscataway, NJ 08855-1575
http://www.LumosLearning.com

Email: support@lumoslearning.com
Tel: (732) 384-0146
Fax: (866) 283-6471

Developed by Expert Teachers

INTRODUCTION

This book is specifically designed to improve student achievement on the State of Texas Assessment of Academic Readiness (STAAR). With over a decade of expertise in developing practice resources for standardized tests, Lumos Learning has designed the most efficient methodology to help students succeed on the state assessments (See Figure 1).

Lumos Smart Test Prep provides students STAAR assessment rehearsal along with an efficient pathway to overcome any standards proficiency gaps. Students perform at their best on standardized tests when they feel comfortable with the test content as well as the test format. Lumos online practice tests are meticulously designed to mirror the STAAR assessment. It adheres to the guidelines provided by the STAAR for the number of questions, standards, difficulty level, sessions, question types, and duration.

The process starts with students taking the online diagnostic assessment. This online diagnostic test will help assess students' proficiency levels in various standards.

After completion of the diagnostic assessment, students can take note of standards where they are not proficient. This step will help parents and educators in developing a targeted remedial study plan based on a student's proficiency gaps.

Once the targeted remedial study plan is in place, students can start practicing the lessons in this workbook that are focused on specific standards.

After the student completes the targeted remedial practice, the student should attempt the second online STAAR practice test. Record the proficiency levels in the second practice test to measure the student progress and identify any additional learning gaps. Further targeted practice can be planned to help students gain comprehensive skills mastery needed to ensure success on the state assessment.

Lumos Smart Test Prep Methodology

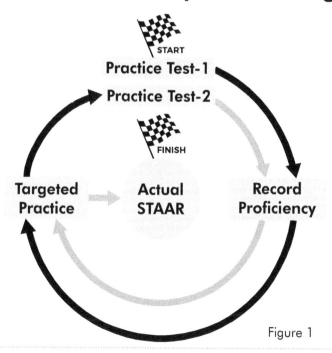

Figure 1

Table of Contents

Sign Up Online

STAAR

Grade 6 ELA Practice

Unlock Digital Access

2 STAAR Practice Tests

5 ELA Strands

Sign Up Now

Url: https://LumosLearning/a/tedbooks

Access Code: G6ESTAAR-95081-P

Access STAAR Test Practice Resources On Your Mobile Device

Online Access

for

STAAR Practice

+

Printed Workbook

for

Skills Practice

Download Lumos StepUp App
from Google Play Store or Apple App Store

After installing the StepUp App, scan this **QR Code** via **tedBook** section of the mobile app

Chapter 1

Lumos Smart Test Prep Methodology

Step 1: Access Online STAAR Practice Test

The online STAAR practice tests mirror the actual State of Texas Assessment of Academic Readiness in the number of questions, item types, test duration, test tools, and more.

After completing the test, your student will receive immediate feedback with detailed reports on standards mastery and a personalized study plan to overcome any learning gaps. With this study plan, use the next section of the workbook to practice.

Use the URL and access code provided below or scan the QR code to access the first STAAR practice test to get started.

URL	QR Code
Visit the URL below and place the book access code **http://www.lumoslearning.com/a/tedbooks** **Access Code: G6ESTAAR-95081-P**	

Step 2: Review the Personalized Study Plan Online

After students complete the online Practice Test 1, they can access their individualized study plan from the table of contents (Figure 2) Parents and Teachers can also review the study plan through their Lumos account (parent or teacher) portal.

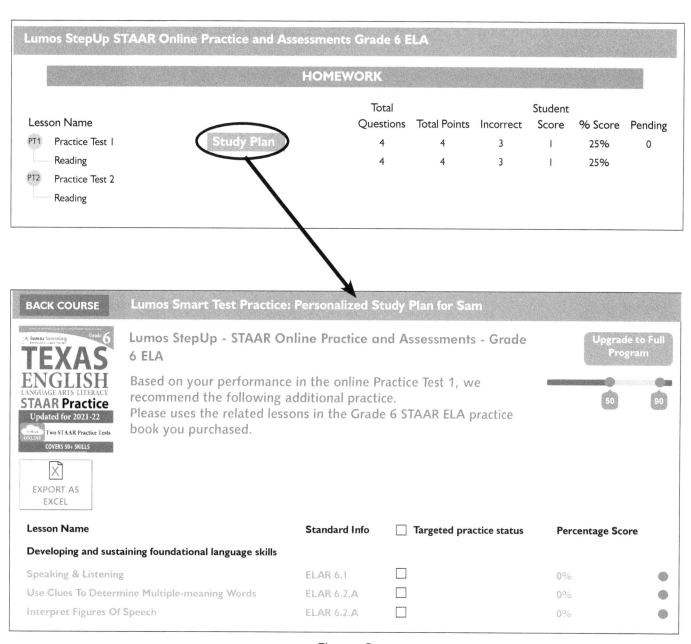

Figure 2

Step 3: Complete Targeted Practice

Using the information provided in the study plan report, complete the targeted practice using the appropriate lessons to overcome proficiency gaps. With lesson names included in the study plan, find the appropriate topics in this workbook and answer the questions provided. Students can refer to the answer key and detailed answers provided for each lesson to gain further understanding of the learning objective. Marking the completed lessons in the study plan after each practice session is recommended.(See Figure 3)

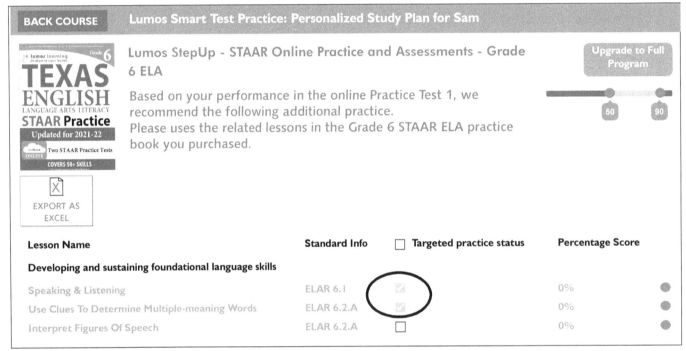

Figure 3

Step 4: Access the Practice Test 2 Online

After completing the targeted practice in this workbook, students should attempt the second STAAR practice test online. Using the student login name and password, login to the Lumos website to complete the second practice test.

Step 5: Repeat Targeted Practice

Repeat the targeted practice as per Step 3 using the second study plan report for Practice test 2 after completion of the second STAAR rehearsal.

Visit http://www.lumoslearning.com/a/lstp for more information on Lumos Smart Test Prep Methodology or Scan the QR Code

Test Taking Tips

1) **The day before the test,** make sure you get a good night's sleep.

2) **On the day of the test,** be sure to eat a good hearty breakfast! Also, be sure to arrive at school on time.

3) **During the test:**

- **Read every question carefully.**

  - Do not spend too much time on any one question. Work steadily through all questions in the section.
  - Attempt all of the questions even if you are not sure of some answers.
  - If you run into a difficult question, eliminate as many choices as you can and then pick the best one from the remaining choices. Intelligent guessing will help you increase your score.
  - Also, mark the question so that if you have extra time, you can return to it after you reach the end of the section.
  - Some questions may refer to a graph, chart, or other kind of picture. Carefully review the graphic before answering the question.
  - Be sure to include explanations for your written responses and show all work.

- **While Answering Multiple-Choice questions.**

  - Read the question completely.
  - Go through the answer choices.
  - If you are struggling with picking out a correct answer, it is best to eliminate some of the choices. At least try to eliminate two of the choices.
  - Reread the question and find support from the passage to support one of the answers.
  - Recheck the question and your answer.

Note: The Texas STAAR Math assessments also includes Grid In type questions in the pencil and paper version of the test.

Chapter 2

Developing and Sustaining Foundational Language Skills

Chapter 2

Lesson 4: Use Context Clue To Determine Word Meaning

Julio was happy and astounded when he won MVP for the soccer season. He had been sure that Reuben or Carlos were going to be chosen.

1. The word "astounded" in this context means: _____.

- Ⓐ disappointed
- Ⓑ very surprised
- Ⓒ satisfied
- Ⓓ pleased

A spider web may look flimsy, but spider silk is actually five times stronger than steel. It is tougher, stronger, and more flexible than anything humans have been able to produce.

2. The word "flimsy" in this context means: _____.

- Ⓐ beautiful
- Ⓑ silky
- Ⓒ weak
- Ⓓ inflexible

New Jersey is on the east coast of the Mid-Atlantic region of the United States of America. It is bordered by the Atlantic Ocean to the east and by Delaware to the southwest, Pennsylvania to the west, and New York to the north and northeast. Parts of the state are suburbs of New York City, just across the Hudson River to the northeast, and Philadelphia, just across the Delaware River on the southwest.

3. In the above context, "bordered" means _____.

- Ⓐ surrounded by
- Ⓑ marked by
- Ⓒ differentiated by
- Ⓓ separated by

Africa is a very diverse continent, with each country, or even each part of a country, having its own unique culture. While it is common for people in the West to refer to Africa as if it was a single country, one should remember the sheer size of the continent. Africa is not one country but 55 different countries, meaning that it is impossible to make generalizations about Africa as a whole.

4. **In the above context, "sheer" means _____.**

   Ⓐ vast
   Ⓑ transparent
   Ⓒ unmixed
   Ⓓ small

My dog is devoted to my family. He would never leave us.

5. **In the above context, "devoted" means _____.**

   Ⓐ loyal
   Ⓑ loving
   Ⓒ unloving
   Ⓓ hated

It is always beneficial to eat your vegetables. That's why your doctor tells you to eat plenty of fruits and vegetables.

6. **In the above context, "beneficial" means _____.**

   Ⓐ horrible
   Ⓑ wrong
   Ⓒ good for you
   Ⓓ nice

The stench coming from the garbage can was unbearable.

7. **In the above context, "stench" means _____.**

   Ⓐ sugary
   Ⓑ freshness
   Ⓒ sweetness
   Ⓓ stink

The celebrity walked the red carpet and was overwhelmed by the barrage of questions from reporters.

8. In the above context, "barrage" means _____.

Ⓐ abundance
Ⓑ few
Ⓒ twenty
Ⓓ little

The sweltering summer heat made the beach unpleasant.

9. In the above context, "sweltering" means _____.

Ⓐ cold
Ⓑ frigid
Ⓒ hot
Ⓓ humid

The big, nasty creature was brown and hairy; it looked hideous.

10. In the above context, 'hideous' means _____.

Ⓐ Ugly
Ⓑ Pretty
Ⓒ Sad
Ⓓ Beautiful

Chapter 2

Lesson 5: Use Common Roots And Affixes

1. **Which of the following is a true statement?**

   Ⓐ A suffix or ending is an affix, which is placed at the end of a word.
   Ⓑ A prefix or beginning is an affix, which is placed at the beginning of a word.
   Ⓒ A suffix is attached at the beginning of the word.
   Ⓓ Both A and B

2. **When the suffix "-able" is added to the word "cap", it means**

   Ⓐ to do something
   Ⓑ to do anything
   Ⓒ not able to do something
   Ⓓ not able to do anything

3. **Identify the suffix in the following words:**

   Salvage, Storage, Forage

   Ⓐ A
   Ⓑ ge
   Ⓒ age
   Ⓓ rage

4. **Identify the prefix in the following words.**

   Anarchy, Anonymous, Anemia

   Ⓐ Anna
   Ⓑ An
   Ⓒ Ana
   Ⓓ Both A and B

5. What does the suffix "less" mean?

- Ⓐ Too little
- Ⓑ With
- Ⓒ Without
- Ⓓ None of the above

6. What does the suffix "ology" mean?

- Ⓐ Study
- Ⓑ Vocabulary
- Ⓒ Sadness
- Ⓓ Study of animals

7. Identify the meaning of the root word in the following words:

Commemorate, Commune, Community

- Ⓐ Far apart
- Ⓑ Uncommon
- Ⓒ Together
- Ⓓ Unlikely

8. Which of the following statements is true?

- Ⓐ The first rule of decoding words is to find out if the word has any suffixes or prefixes
- Ⓑ You should always divide between the consonants
- Ⓒ Both A and B
- Ⓓ None of the above

9. Using the rule 'divide between the consonants', decode the word 'sentence'.

- Ⓐ se-n-tence
- Ⓑ sen-tence
- Ⓒ sen-ten-ce
- Ⓓ none of the above

10. What is the correct way to decode the word 'Monarch'?

- Ⓐ mona-rch
- Ⓑ mon-ar-ch
- Ⓒ mon-a-rch
- Ⓓ mon-arch

Chapter 2

Lesson 6: Determine The Meaning Of A Word

1. **What does the underlined word in the sentence mean?**

   Johnny was certain he hadn't <u>misplaced</u> his glove but he couldn't find it.

   Ⓐ found
   Ⓑ lost
   Ⓒ hid
   Ⓓ borrowed

2. **What does the underlined word in the sentence mean?**

   Despite the brisk temperatures, football fans still packed the stadium to watch the championship game.

   Ⓐ hot
   Ⓑ fast
   Ⓒ cool
   Ⓓ exciting

3. **What does the underlined word in the sentence mean?**

   Natalie and Sophia couldn't wait to ride the roller coaster. They'd heard it was very <u>exhilarating</u>.

   Ⓐ fast
   Ⓑ frightening
   Ⓒ exciting
   Ⓓ boring

4. **What does the underlined word in the sentence mean?**

   Billy always found raking leaves to be a very <u>mundane</u> chore. It was the same thing over and over.

   Ⓐ fast
   Ⓑ frightening
   Ⓒ exciting
   Ⓓ boring

5. What does the underlined word in the sentence mean?

The whimpering puppies were clearly <u>ravenous</u>. They devoured the food when it was ready.

Ⓐ hungry
Ⓑ sleepy
Ⓒ playful
Ⓓ scared

6. What does the underlined word in the sentence mean?

The basketball team had <u>triumphed</u> over their opponents.

Ⓐ lost
Ⓑ forfeited
Ⓒ competed
Ⓓ won

7. What does the underlined word in the sentence mean?

Abby found the new student to be <u>bewitching</u>.

Ⓐ scary
Ⓑ charming
Ⓒ kind
Ⓓ boring

8. What does the underlined word in the sentence mean?

Julia found fishing to be completely <u>repulsing</u>. She wanted nothing to do with putting the worm on the hook.

Ⓐ wonderful
Ⓑ delightful
Ⓒ relaxing
Ⓓ awful

9. **What does the underlined word in the sentence mean?**

As Tony and Steve climbed higher and higher up the mountainside, they noticed everything took on a whole new <u>perspective</u>.

Ⓐ appearance
Ⓑ experience
Ⓒ height
Ⓓ altitude

10. **If you do not know what a word means, where can you look?**

Ⓐ Dictionary
Ⓑ Thesaurus
Ⓒ Glossary
Ⓓ All of the above

Chapter 2

Lesson 7: Use Relationships To Better Understand Words

1. **Identify the cause and the effect in the following sentence:**

   The blizzard was so widespread that all flights were canceled.

   Ⓐ cause-blizzard; effect- flights canceled
   Ⓑ cause-flights; effect- blizzard
   Ⓒ cause-blizzard; effect- flights
   Ⓓ cause-canceled flights; effect- widespread blizzard

2. **Identify the cause and the effect in the following sentence:**

   Several hundred people were left homeless by the flood.

   Ⓐ cause- homeless people; effect -flood
   Ⓑ cause- flood; effect - people left homeless
   Ⓒ cause- people; effect -homeless
   Ⓓ cause- flood; effect -several hundred people

3. **Identify the cause and the effect in the following sentence:**

   Pedro's friendly attitude got him the job.

   Ⓐ cause- Pedro; effect- friendly attitude
   Ⓑ cause- Pedro; effect- got the job
   Ⓒ cause- friendly attitude; effect- got the job
   Ⓓ cause- job; effect- friendly attitude

4. **Choose the correct animal which belongs to the category of mammals:** _____

   Ⓐ giraffe
   Ⓑ cheese
   Ⓒ frogs
   Ⓓ bees

5. Choose the correct item which belongs to the category of birds: _____

    Ⓐ parrots
    Ⓑ giraffes
    Ⓒ bees
    Ⓓ sharks

6. Choose the correct item which belongs to the category of desserts: _____

    Ⓐ elephants
    Ⓑ pie
    Ⓒ carrots
    Ⓓ cheese

7. This exercise will help you practice identifying parts and wholes.
Arrange the following words in order by size:

galaxy, universe, county, country, town, neighborhood, state, world, continent, solar system, hemisphere.

which is part of a _____,
which is part of a _____,
which is part of a _____,
which is part of a _____,
which is part of a _____,
which is part of a _____,
which is part of a _____,
which is part of a _____,
which is part of a _____,
which is part of a _____,
which is part of a _____.

    Ⓐ town; neighborhood; county; state; country; continent; galaxy; hemisphere; world; universe; solar system
    Ⓑ world; solar system; galaxy; universe; neighborhood; town; county; state; country; continent; hemisphere;
    Ⓒ neighborhood; town; county; state; country; continent; hemisphere; world; solar system; galaxy; universe
    Ⓓ neighborhood; galaxy; universe; town; county; state; country; hemisphere; world; solar system; continent

8. **Choose the correct item which belongs to the category of insects:** _____

   Ⓐ sharks
   Ⓑ bees
   Ⓒ frogs
   Ⓓ parrots

9. **Identify the cause and the effect in the following sentence:**

   The burned popcorn made the whole house smell like smoke.

   Ⓐ cause-popcorn; effect- smoke
   Ⓑ cause- burned popcorn; effect- smoky smell
   Ⓒ cause-house; effect- burned popcorn
   Ⓓ cause-smoky smell; effect- burned popcorn

10. **Identify the cause and the effect in the following sentence:**

    He practiced until he could make 3 out of 4 free throws.

    Ⓐ cause- free throws; effect-practice
    Ⓑ cause- practice; effect- four free throws
    Ⓒ cause- practice; effect- make three out of four free throws
    Ⓓ cause- free throws; effect- three throws

Chapter 2

Lesson 8: Maintain Consistency In Style And Tone

1. **Which of the following sentences paints the clearest picture?**

    Ⓐ Even though the sun was shining, Mary couldn't help but feel chilled by the cool morning breeze.
    Ⓑ Even though the sun was shining, Mary was still cold.
    Ⓒ The sun was shining but the breeze made Mary cold.
    Ⓓ Mary was chilled on the sunny, yet breeze morning.

2. **Which of the following sentences uses the most descriptive words and style?**

    Ⓐ As the darkness fell, Scott was scared of what might be out there.
    Ⓑ As the darkness fell, Scott couldn't help but be wary of what might lurk out there in the shadows.
    Ⓒ As the darkness fell, Scott was frightened by what he could not see.
    Ⓓ Scott is scared of the dark.

3. **Which of the following sentences provides the most detail about the topic?**

    Ⓐ Callie loved the smell of cookies.
    Ⓑ Callie loved the smell of her mother's cookies.
    Ⓒ Callie loved the smell of her mother's fresh baked cookies.
    Ⓓ Callie loved the smell of her mother's fresh baked chocolate chip cookies.

4. **Which of the following sentences provides sufficient information in an efficient format?**

    Ⓐ George Washington was the first president. He was also a general in the American Revolution.
    Ⓑ George Washington was not only the first president, but he was also a general in the American Revolution.
    Ⓒ George Washington was a general and president.
    Ⓓ George Washington was the first president and a general in the American Revolution.

5. **Which of the following sentences is most concise?**

    Ⓐ I loved the movie. I just didn't like the surprise ending.
    Ⓑ I loved the movie, and I just didn't like the surprise ending.
    Ⓒ I loved the movie, but I just didn't like the surprise ending.
    Ⓓ I loved the movie, but I didn't like the surprise ending.

6. **Which of the following sentences is the most concise and accurate?**

    Ⓐ I'm so nervous for the play. What if I forget my lines? What if I fall down and everyone laughs at me?
    Ⓑ I'm so nervous for the play. What if I forget my lines, fall down, and everyone laughs at me?
    Ⓒ I'm so nervous for the play. What if I forget my lines or fall down and everyone laughs at me?
    Ⓓ I am nervous that I will forget my lines. I am nervous I will fall down and everyone will laugh at me.

7. **Which of the following sentences provides the most imaginative style?**

    Ⓐ After the dog got out of the yard, Freddie ran after it.
    Ⓑ The dog got out of the yard. Freddie ran after it.
    Ⓒ Freddie ran after the dog, after it got out of the yard.
    Ⓓ The dog got out of the yard and Freddie ran after it.

8. **Which of the following sentences provides the most detailed concise expression of the events?**

    Ⓐ Seth and Iris walked on the beach. They collected sea shells.
    Ⓑ As they walked along the beach, Seth and Iris collected sea shells.
    Ⓒ Seth and Iris walked and collected sea shells.
    Ⓓ At the beach, Seth and Iris walked. They also collected sea shells.

9. **Which of the following sentences is the most concise?**

    Ⓐ Beth thought the test was hard and difficult. Mary thought the test was easy.
    Ⓑ While Beth thought the test was challenging, Mary thought it was easy.
    Ⓒ Beth thought the test was hard and Mary thought it was easy.
    Ⓓ Beth thought the test was hard and difficult, but Mary thought the test was easy.

10. Which of the following sentences uses the smoothest and most concise language to describe the event?

Ⓐ The lights slowly darkened to signal the start of the movie. Mark and Anthony got excited.

Ⓑ The lights slowly darkened to signal the start of the movie, and Mark and Anthony got excited.

Ⓒ Mark and Anthony got excited when the lights slowly darkened to signal the start of the movie.

Ⓓ The lights went out so the movie could start. Mark and Anthony got excited.

Chapter 2

Lesson 9: Consult Reference Materials

1. **Alphabetize the following words:**

   hibiscus, petunia, rose, honeysuckle, daffodil

   Ⓐ hibiscus, petunia, rose, honeysuckle, daffodil
   Ⓑ daffodil, hibiscus, honeysuckle, petunia, rose
   Ⓒ daffodil, honeysuckle, hibiscus, petunia, rose
   Ⓓ hibiscus, petunia, rose, daffodil, honeysuckle

2. **Alphabetize the following words:**

   mouse, mule, monkey, moose, mole

   Ⓐ mouse, monkey, moose, mole, mule
   Ⓑ mouse, mule, monkey, moose, mole
   Ⓒ mouse, moose, monkey, mole, mule
   Ⓓ mole, monkey, moose, mouse, mule

3. **Alphabetize the following words:**

   sustain, solicit, sizzle, sanitize, secure

   Ⓐ sustain, solicit, sizzle, sanitize, secure
   Ⓑ sanitize, secure, sustain, solicit, sizzle
   Ⓒ sanitize, solicit, sizzle, sustain, secure
   Ⓓ sanitize, secure, sizzle, solicit, sustain

4. **The dictionary contains _____.**

   Ⓐ meaning of a word
   Ⓑ pronunciation of a word
   Ⓒ the etymology (where the word came from)
   Ⓓ all the above

5. **Which of the following answer choices can you find in a thesaurus?**

    Ⓐ homonym
    Ⓑ homograph
    Ⓒ synonym
    Ⓓ definition

6. **How do you go about starting to find a word you are looking for in the dictionary?**

    Ⓐ Open the dictionary
    Ⓑ Open the dictionary to the page that has the first two letters of the word you are looking for
    Ⓒ Open the dictionary to the page that has the last two letters of the word
    Ⓓ Open the dictionary and look in the table of contents

7. **What are guidewords in a dictionary?**

    Ⓐ Guidewords are words that tell you how to pronounce your word
    Ⓑ Guidewords are located at the bottom of each page
    Ⓒ Guidewords are words that tell you the part of speech of your word
    Ⓓ Guidewords are at the top of each page to tell you the first and last words you will find on that page.

8. **How many syllables are in the word "organized?"**

    Ⓐ 3
    Ⓑ 4
    Ⓒ 6
    Ⓓ 1

9. **How many syllables are in the word "jacket?"**

    Ⓐ 1
    Ⓑ 3
    Ⓒ 2
    Ⓓ 4

10. **How many syllables would you have, if you divide the word 'hyacinth'?**

    Ⓐ 2
    Ⓑ 3
    Ⓒ 8
    Ⓓ 4

Chapter 2

Lesson 10: Recognize Variations In English

1. **What is the correct way to write the underlined part of the following sentence?**

   Yesterday my mom baked cookies and we <u>eat</u> them all.

   Ⓐ will eat
   Ⓑ did eat
   Ⓒ eaten
   Ⓓ ate

2. **What is the correct way to write the underlined part of the following sentence?**

   Jenny went to the store and <u>buy</u> apples, milk, and bread.

   Ⓐ bought
   Ⓑ will buy
   Ⓒ did buy
   Ⓓ buyed

3. **What is the correct way to write the underlined part of the following sentence?**

   Billy and Matt rode <u>they're</u> bikes to the park.

   Ⓐ there
   Ⓑ their
   Ⓒ they
   Ⓓ them

4. **What is the correct way to write the underlined part of the following sentence?**

   My dad and I <u>builds</u> a tree house together this weekend.

   Ⓐ will build
   Ⓑ built
   Ⓒ had built
   Ⓓ build

5. **What is the correct way to write the underlined part of the following sentence?**

They always take such good care of <u>them</u> garden.

Ⓐ that
Ⓑ there
Ⓒ they're
Ⓓ their

6. **What is the correct way to write the underlined part of the sentence?**

Tony and Melissa had fun <u>sing</u> in the spring concert.

Ⓐ sung
Ⓑ singing
Ⓒ sang
Ⓓ will sing

7. **What is the correct way to write the underlined part of the sentence?**

Debbie always <u>did</u> her homework first thing when she gets home.

Ⓐ does
Ⓑ will do
Ⓒ doesn't do
Ⓓ didn't

8. **What is the correct way to write the underlined part of the sentence?**

Mickey's brother always takes <u>him</u> toys.

Ⓐ her
Ⓑ he
Ⓒ their
Ⓓ his

9. **What is the correct way to write the underlined part of the sentence?**

<u>Them</u> holiday lights are so pretty and sparkly.

Ⓐ They
Ⓑ Her
Ⓒ Those
Ⓓ All

10. What is the correct way to write the underlined part of the sentence?

My dog always runs <u>happy</u> by my side.

Ⓐ with happy
Ⓑ happier
Ⓒ happiest
Ⓓ happily

Chapter 2

Lesson 11: Distinguish Between Word Associations And Definitions

1. **Denotation of a word is the _____.**

   Ⓐ slang for a word.
   Ⓑ literal meaning.
   Ⓒ part of speech of a word.
   Ⓓ feelings we have about a word.

2. **Connotation refers to _____.**

   Ⓐ the literal meaning of a word.
   Ⓑ the part of speech of a word.
   Ⓒ how we feel about a word.
   Ⓓ the slang meaning of a word.

3. **Which of the following words has the same denotative meaning as the word house?**

   Ⓐ dwelling
   Ⓑ abode
   Ⓒ residence
   Ⓓ All of the above

4. **Which of the following words has the same denotative meaning as the word child?**

   Ⓐ elderly
   Ⓑ ancient
   Ⓒ adolescent
   Ⓓ None of the above

5. **Which of the following words have the same denotation?**

   Ⓐ smelly; smiley
   Ⓑ sweet; sweat
   Ⓒ trash; garbage
   Ⓓ stubborn; easy-going

6. Which of the following words have the same denotation?

- Ⓐ expensive; cheap
- Ⓑ short; tall
- Ⓒ rabbit; horse
- Ⓓ curious; nosy

7. Which of the following words has the same denotation but a negative connotation?

The word "inexpensive" has a positive connotation.

- Ⓐ costly
- Ⓑ expensive
- Ⓒ free
- Ⓓ cheap

8. Which of the following words has the same denotation but a positive connotation?

The word "disaster" has a negative connotation.

- Ⓐ Catastrophe
- Ⓑ Flop
- Ⓒ Emergency
- Ⓓ Tragedy

9. Which of the following words has the same denotation but a negative connotation?

The word "messy" has a positive connotation.

- Ⓐ Filthy
- Ⓑ Disorganized
- Ⓒ Muddled
- Ⓓ Sloppy

10. Which of the following words has the same denotation but a positive connotation?

The word "old" has a negative connotation.

- Ⓐ Decrepit
- Ⓑ Ancient
- Ⓒ Elderly
- Ⓓ Over the hill

Chapter 2

Lesson 12: Vary Sentence

1. **What is the best way to combine the following sentences?**

   The oven temperature was too hot. The cookies got burnt.

   Ⓐ The oven temperature was too hot, the cookies got burnt.
   Ⓑ The oven temperature was too hot because the cookies got burnt.
   Ⓒ The oven temperature was too hot the cookies got burnt.
   Ⓓ The oven temperature was too hot, so the cookies got burnt.

2. **What is the best way to combine the following sentences?**

   Mike and Johnny wanted to play outside. It was raining so they couldn't.

   Ⓐ Mike and Johnny wanted to play outside, but it was raining.
   Ⓑ Because of the rain, Mike and Johnny couldn't play outside.
   Ⓒ Mike and Johnny wanted to play outside and it was raining so they couldn't.
   Ⓓ Mike and Johnny wanted to play outside in the rain.

3. **What is the best way to combine the following sentences?**

   I would like to have pizza at my party. I would also like to have ice cream and chocolate cake.

   Ⓐ I would like to have pizza at my party, and I would also like to have ice cream and chocolate cake.
   Ⓑ I would like to have pizza at my party, and ice cream and chocolate cake.
   Ⓒ I would like to have pizza, ice cream, and chocolate cake at my party.
   Ⓓ At my party, I would like to have pizza and ice cream and chocolate cake.

4. **What is the best way to combine the following sentences?**

   We should go to the mall. After school.

   Ⓐ After school, we should go to the mall.
   Ⓑ We should go to the mall, after school.
   Ⓒ We should go to the mall, and after school.
   Ⓓ After school, to the mall we should go.

5. **Which is the best way to combine the following sentences?**

The cat chases the dog. The dog chases the cat.

Ⓐ The cat chases the dog, and the dog chases the cat.
Ⓑ The cat chases the dog, but the dog chases the cat.
Ⓒ The cat chases the dog, the dog chases the cat.
Ⓓ The cat and dog chase each other.

6. **Which is the best way to combine the following sentences?**

Summer is nice. Spring is my favorite.

Ⓐ Summer is nice, and spring is my favorite.
Ⓑ Summer is nice, spring is my favorite.
Ⓒ Summer is nice, but spring is my favorite.
Ⓓ Summer and spring are nice.

7. **Which is the best way to combine the following sentences?**

We will be going camping. After school on Friday.

Ⓐ We will be going camping, and after school on Friday.
Ⓑ After school on Friday, we will be going camping.
Ⓒ After school on Friday we will be going camping.
Ⓓ Camping we are going after school on Friday.

8. **Which is the best way to combine the following sentences?**

Before the party I have to wash the dishes. I also have to do the laundry. And walk the dog.

Ⓐ Before the party I have to wash the dishes. I also have to do the laundry and walk the dog.
Ⓑ Before the party I have to wash the dishes do the laundry and walk the dog.
Ⓒ Before the party, I have to wash the dishes, do the laundry and walk the dog.
Ⓓ I have to wash the dishes. I also have to do the laundry and walk the dog. Before the party.

9. **Which is the best way to combine the following sentences?**

Lisa got a book. She got it at the library.

Ⓐ Lisa got a book at the library.
Ⓑ Lisa got a book, and she got it at the library.
Ⓒ Lisa got a book, so she got it at the library.
Ⓓ At the library, Lisa got her book.

10. Which is the best way to combine the following sentences?

The puppy was soft and cuddly. It was brown.

Ⓐ The puppy was soft and cuddly, and it was brown.
Ⓑ The brown puppy was soft and cuddly.
Ⓒ The puppy was soft and cuddly and brown.
Ⓓ The puppy was brown and it was soft and it was cuddly.

Chapter 2

Lesson 13: Correct Subject-verb Agreement

1. **Correct the following sentence to show subject-verb agreement.**

   Tracy and Gary likes to solve puzzles.

   Ⓐ Tracy and Gary likes to solve puzzles.
   Ⓑ Tracy and Gary like to solve puzzles.
   Ⓒ Tracy and Gary like to solves puzzle.
   Ⓓ Tracy likes to solve puzzle.

2. **Correct the following sentence to show subject-verb agreement.**

   All of the students competes for the prizes.

   Ⓐ All of the student competes for the prizes.
   Ⓑ All of the students compete for the prizes.
   Ⓒ The students competes for the prizes.
   Ⓓ None of the above

3. **Correct the following sentence to show subject-verb agreement.**

   Many people considers tea a stimulant.

   Ⓐ Many a people considers tea a stimulant.
   Ⓑ Many people consider tea a stimulant.
   Ⓒ Many peoples consider tea a stimulant.
   Ⓓ The above sentence needs no correction.

4. **Correct the verb to show correct subject-verb agreement.**

   The enemies plots revenge and won the battle this time.

   Ⓐ The enemy plot revenge and win the battle this time.
   Ⓑ The enemy plot revenge and will win the battle this time.
   Ⓒ The enemy will plot revenge and will won the battle this time.
   Ⓓ The enemies plot revenge and win the battle this time.

5. Correct the following sentence to make it correct.

Sally finish her project earlier than the others.

Ⓐ Sally finish her projects earlier than the others.
Ⓑ Sally finished her project earlier than the others.
Ⓒ Sally have already finish her project earlier than the others.
Ⓓ Sally finishing her project earlier than the others.

6. Fill in the blank with the correct word that fits in the sentence.

Some of the votes _____ to have been miscounted.

Ⓐ seems
Ⓑ seem
Ⓒ will seem
Ⓓ shall seem

7. Fill in the blank with the correct word that fits in the sentence.

All of the dancers_____ to be sick.

Ⓐ appear
Ⓑ has appeared
Ⓒ will appear
Ⓓ appears

8. Fill in the blank with the correct word that fits in the sentence.

Parents and students _____ against the hike in tuition fee.

Ⓐ is
Ⓑ are
Ⓒ are being
Ⓓ had been

9. Fill in the blank with the correct word that fits in the sentence.

Either the Principal in this School or the Chief Administrator _____ to make a quick decision.

Ⓐ have
Ⓑ will
Ⓒ has
Ⓓ are

10. Fill in the blank with the correct word that fits in the sentence.

She seems to forget that there _____ things to be done before the expedition.

Ⓐ is
Ⓑ has
Ⓒ are
Ⓓ have

Chapter 2

Lesson 14: Correct Use Of Adjectives And Adverbs

1. Identify the adjective in the following sentence.

The book that I was reading had colorful pages.

- Ⓐ colorful
- Ⓑ reading
- Ⓒ pages
- Ⓓ book

2. Identify the adjective/adjectives in the following sentence.

Earth is the most beautiful planet in the solar system.

- Ⓐ Earth
- Ⓑ beautiful
- Ⓒ system
- Ⓓ planet

3. Identify the adjective in this sentence.

The frightened alien ran back into its airship.

- Ⓐ airship
- Ⓑ alien
- Ⓒ frightened
- Ⓓ ran

4. Identify the adverb in the following sentence.

The mother was quite unhappy to see her son leave.

- Ⓐ quite
- Ⓑ unhappy
- Ⓒ the
- Ⓓ leave

5. Identify the adverb in the following sentence.

The long wait made him utterly tired.

Ⓐ long
Ⓑ wait
Ⓒ tired
Ⓓ utterly

6. Identify the adverb in the following sentence and point out the verb it modifies/describes.

My clever friend answered all the questions correctly.

Ⓐ adverb: clever ; verb: friend
Ⓑ adverb: correctly ; verb: questions
Ⓒ adverb: correctly ; verb: answered
Ⓓ adverb: clever : verb: question

7. Identify the adverb in the following sentence.

The girl politely asked the boy for her book back.

Ⓐ Girl
Ⓑ Book
Ⓒ Politely
Ⓓ Asked

8. Identify the adjective or adjectives in the following sentence.

The polka dot umbrella protected Ted from the cold rain.

Ⓐ polka dot and protected
Ⓑ umbrella and polka dot
Ⓒ umbrella and rain
Ⓓ polka dot and cold

9. Identify the adverb in the following sentence.

Last night, the whole family slept soundly.

Ⓐ soundly
Ⓑ last
Ⓒ slept
Ⓓ night

10. Identify the adverb in the following sentence.

The computer printer hardly works.

(A) Computer
(B) Works
(C) Printer
(D) Hardly

Chapter 2

Lesson 15: Recognize Pronouns

1. **Choose the correct pronoun to complete the sentence.**

    I did it by _____.

    Ⓐ me
    Ⓑ myself
    Ⓒ I
    Ⓓ my

2. **Choose the correct pronoun to complete the sentence.**

    We _____ are responsible for the decorations.

    Ⓐ us
    Ⓑ ourselves
    Ⓒ themselves
    Ⓓ myself

3. **Choose the correct pronoun to complete the sentence.**

    She made up the story _____ .

    Ⓐ himself
    Ⓑ herself
    Ⓒ itself
    Ⓓ themself

4. **Choose the correct pronoun to complete the sentence.**

    If a student wants to do well, _____ to get plenty of sleep.

    Ⓐ you have
    Ⓑ he or she has
    Ⓒ you has
    Ⓓ they have

5. **Choose the correct pronoun to complete the sentence.**

The best poker players can keep _____ faces from showing any reaction.

Ⓐ her
Ⓑ its
Ⓒ their
Ⓓ his

6. **Correct the following sentence to make the referent clear.**

Charlie danced with his friend Carol and Sue most of the evening. She is his girlfriend.

Ⓐ Sue is his girlfriend.
Ⓑ He is her friend.
Ⓒ She is the girlfriend.
Ⓓ Carol is his girlfriend.

7. **Correct the following sentence to make the referent clear.**

Riding without a helmet is a big risk. This is unnecessary.

Ⓐ They are unnecessary.
Ⓑ This risk is unnecessary.
Ⓒ It is unnecessary.
Ⓓ Riding is unnecessary.

8. **Correct the following sentence to make the referent clear.**

The cat ate the goldfish before I could stop the tragedy. It was terrible.

Ⓐ They are terrible.
Ⓑ The tragedy was terrible.
Ⓒ The goldfish was terrible.
Ⓓ The cat was terrible.

9. **Correct the following sentence to make the referent clear.**

Johnny is taller than Ahmed. He's grown a lot this year.

Ⓐ The boys have grown a lot this year.
Ⓑ Ahmed has grown a lot this year.
Ⓒ They have grown a lot this year.
Ⓓ Johnny has grown a lot this year.

10. Correct the following sentence to make the referent clear.

The Sharks and the Jets were the gangs in West Side Story. They performed great dances.

Ⓐ The gangs performed great dances.
Ⓑ The sharks performed great dances.
Ⓒ It performed great dances.
Ⓓ The Jets performed great dances.

Chapter 2

Lesson 16: Recognize And Correct Vague Pronouns

1. **Choose the pronoun that agrees with the antecedent in the following sentence.**

   He forgot _____ homework and will have detention at lunch.

   Ⓐ his
   Ⓑ my
   Ⓒ its
   Ⓓ their

2. **Choose the pronoun that agrees with the antecedent in the following sentence.**

   The students made _____ own costumes for the play.

   Ⓐ her
   Ⓑ their
   Ⓒ my
   Ⓓ our

3. **Choose the pronoun that agrees with the antecedent in the following sentence.**

   Gavin's dog follows _____ everywhere.

   Ⓐ their
   Ⓑ me
   Ⓒ his
   Ⓓ him

4. **Choose the pronoun that agrees with the antecedent in the following sentence.**

   Emily and Nathan both love to sing so _____ are going to do a duet for the talent show.

   Ⓐ they
   Ⓑ he
   Ⓒ she
   Ⓓ their

5. **Choose the pronoun that agrees with the antecedent in the following sentence.**

The students practiced many hours in preparation for _____ concert.

Ⓐ their
Ⓑ there
Ⓒ our
Ⓓ his

6. **Choose the pronoun that agrees with the antecedent in the following sentence.**

Roger stayed up late to finish _____ English project.

Ⓐ our
Ⓑ his
Ⓒ their
Ⓓ my

7. **Choose the pronoun that agrees with the antecedent in the following sentence.**

Mary left the cookies out on the counter so I ate _____.

Ⓐ it
Ⓑ she
Ⓒ them
Ⓓ their

8. **Choose the pronoun that agrees with the antecedent in the following sentence.**

The store was having a huge sale on all _____ shoes.

Ⓐ its
Ⓑ her
Ⓒ our
Ⓓ my

9. **Choose the pronoun that agrees with the antecedent in the following sentence.**

Even though Patty is packed for the trip, _____ does not feel ready to go.

Ⓐ I
Ⓑ she
Ⓒ he
Ⓓ they

10. Choose the pronoun that agrees with the antecedent in the following sentence.

Billy and Luis both forgot to bring _____ sleeping bags on the camping trip.

- Ⓐ his
- Ⓑ my
- Ⓒ our
- Ⓓ their

Chapter 2

Lesson 17: Recognize And Correct Shifts In Pronoun Number And Person

1. **Which pronoun best completes the following sentence?**

   Each student got to choose _____ own desk.

   Ⓐ his/ her
   Ⓑ their
   Ⓒ its

2. **Which pronoun best completes the following sentences?**

   All the girls were excited to be able to wear _____ new dresses to the dance.

   Ⓐ the
   Ⓑ their
   Ⓒ there
   Ⓓ her

3. **Which pronoun best completes the following sentence?**

   Coach Bob was proud of the way _____ team played in the game.

   Ⓐ their
   Ⓑ our
   Ⓒ her
   Ⓓ his

4. **Which pronoun best completes the following sentence?**

   Billy and _____ plan to ride our bikes to the park as soon as school is out.

   Ⓐ I
   Ⓑ me
   Ⓒ us
   Ⓓ his

5. Which pronoun best completes the following sentence?

Mrs. Marshall's students won the reading contest. _____ read more books than any other class in the sixth grade.

Ⓐ Their
Ⓑ Her
Ⓒ They
Ⓓ I

6. Which pronoun best completes the following sentence?

Johnny's friends are all on the football team with _____.

Ⓐ her
Ⓑ his
Ⓒ it
Ⓓ him

7. Which pronoun best completes the following sentence?

Lucy loves to have pepperoni and onions with extra cheese on _____ pizza.

Ⓐ her
Ⓑ their
Ⓒ his
Ⓓ my

8. Which pronoun best completes the following sentence?

_____ can't wait to go to see my Aunt Sara for the holidays.

Ⓐ We
Ⓑ He
Ⓒ I
Ⓓ They

9. Which pronoun best completes the following sentence?

When Tiffany went ice skating, _____ fell and twisted her ankle.

Ⓐ she
Ⓑ her
Ⓒ my
Ⓓ we

10. Which pronoun best completes the following sentence?

My dog loves playing catch with his ball, except _____ never brings it back.

- Ⓐ they
- Ⓑ she
- Ⓒ he
- Ⓓ I

Chapter 2

Lesson 18: Demonstrate Command Of Capitalization

1. **Choose the answer with the correct placement of capital letters for the sentence below.**

   my doctor moved to phoenix, arizona.

   Ⓐ my doctor moved to phoenix, arizona.
   Ⓑ My doctor moved to Phoenix, Arizona.
   Ⓒ My doctor moved to phoenix, arizona.
   Ⓓ My doctor moved to phoenix, arizona.

2. **Choose the answer with the correct placement of capital letters for the sentence below.**

   my mother called doctor billings to make an appointment for saturday.

   Ⓐ My mother called Doctor Billings to make an appointment for Saturday.
   Ⓑ my mother called doctor billings to make an appointment for Saturday.
   Ⓒ My mother called doctor billings to make an appointment for saturday.
   Ⓓ My mother called doctor Billings to make an appointment for Saturday.

3. **Choose the answer with the correct placement of capital letters for the sentence below.**

   mother says he is the best doctor in santa maria.

   Ⓐ Mother says he is the best doctor in santa maria.
   Ⓑ Mother says he is the best doctor in Santa maria.
   Ⓒ Mother says he is the best doctor in Santa Maria.
   Ⓓ mother says he is the best Doctor in Santa maria.

4. **Choose the answer with the correct placement of capital letters for the sentence below.**

   the principal made pablo captain of the safety patrol.

   Ⓐ The principal made pablo captain of the safety patrol.
   Ⓑ The principal made Pablo Captain of the Safety Patrol.
   Ⓒ The principal made pablo captain of the Safety Patrol.
   Ⓓ The principal made Pablo captain of the safety patrol.

5. Choose the answer with the correct placement of capital letters for the sentence below.

captain jones of the american legion spoke at martin luther king, jr. elementary school.

Ⓐ Captain Jones of the American Legion spoke at Martin Luther King, Jr. Elementary School.
Ⓑ Captain jones of the american legion spoke at martin luther king, jr. elementary school.
Ⓒ Captain jones of the American Legion spoke at martin luther king, jr. elementary school.
Ⓓ Captain jones of the American legion spoke at Martin luther king, Jr. elementary school.

6. Choose the answer with the correct placement of capital letters for the sentence below.

dad, can you help me for a minute?

Ⓐ dad, can you help me for a minute?
Ⓑ Dad, Can You help Me for a Minute?
Ⓒ Dad, can you help me for a Minute?
Ⓓ Dad, can you help me for a minute?

7. Choose the answer with the correct placement of capital letters for the sentence below.

mom said angela can spend the night on friday.

Ⓐ Mom said angela can spend the night on friday.
Ⓑ Mom said Angela can spend the night on Friday.
Ⓒ Mom said Angela can spend the night on friday.
Ⓓ Mom said Angela can spend the Night on friday.

8. Choose the answer with the correct placement of capital letters for the sentence below.

my grandma made a german chocolate cake for sunday dinner.

Ⓐ My grandma made a german chocolate cake for sunday dinner.
Ⓑ My Grandma made a german chocolate cake for sunday dinner.
Ⓒ My grandma made a German chocolate cake for Sunday dinner.
Ⓓ my grandma made a german chocolate cake for Sunday dinner.

9. Choose the answer with the correct placement of capital letters for the sentence below.

kathy barrett lives on stanley street next door to domino's pizza.

Ⓐ Kathy Barrett lives on Stanley Street next door to Domino's Pizza.
Ⓑ Kathy barrett lives on stanley street next door to domino's pizza.
Ⓒ Kathy Barrett lives on stanley street next door to domino's pizza.
Ⓓ Kathy barrett lives on stanley street next door to Domino's pizza.

10. Choose the answer with the correct placement of capital letters for the sentence below.

michael read the call of the wild in july.

Ⓐ michael read the call of the wild in July.
Ⓑ Michael read The Call of the Wild in July.
Ⓒ Michael read the call of the wild in july.
Ⓓ Michael read The call of the wild in july.

Chapter 2

Lesson 19: Demonstrate Command Of Punctuation

1. **Choose the answer with the correct punctuation for the sentence below.**

    Hi, Mom I'm home called Robby as he walked through the door

    Ⓐ "Hi, Mom! I'm home," called Robby as he walked through the door.
    Ⓑ Hi, Mom I'm home called Robby as he walked through the door.
    Ⓒ Hi Mom I'm home, called Robby as he walked through the door.
    Ⓓ Hi Mom, I'm home, called Robby, as he walked through the door.

2. **Choose the answer with the correct punctuation for the sentence below.**

    I had bananas oranges and cherries in the refrigerator but they're all gone

    Ⓐ I had bananas oranges and cherries in the refrigerator but they're all gone.
    Ⓑ I had bananas oranges and cherries in the refrigerator, but they're all gone.
    Ⓒ I had bananas, oranges, and cherries in the refrigerator, but they're all gone.
    Ⓓ I had bananas oranges and cherries, in the refrigerator, but they're all gone.

3. **Choose the answer with the correct punctuation for the sentence below.**

    September is the busiest month of the year that's why it's my favorite

    Ⓐ September is the busiest month of the year; that's why it's my favorite.
    Ⓑ September is the busiest month of the year that's why it's my favorite.
    Ⓒ September, is the busiest month of the year, that's why it's my favorite.
    Ⓓ September is the busiest month of the year that's why it's my favorite!

4. **Choose the answer with the correct punctuation for the sentence below.**

    Which one is Olivias jacket the teacher asked

    Ⓐ Which one is Olivias jacket the teacher asked?
    Ⓑ Which one is Olivia's jacket the teacher asked.
    Ⓒ "Which one is Olivia's jacket?" the teacher asked.
    Ⓓ Which one is Olivia's jacket the teacher asked!

5. **Choose the answer with the correct punctuation for the sentence below.**

New Years Day will be on January 1 2012

Ⓐ New Years Day will be on January 1 2012.
Ⓑ New Year's Day will be on January 1, 2012.
Ⓒ New Years Day will be on January, 1, 2012.
Ⓓ New Year's Day, will be on January 1, 2012.

6. **Choose the answer with the correct punctuation for the sentence below.**

I got into a great college which made my mom happy.

Ⓐ I got in, to a great college which made, my mom happy.
Ⓑ I got in to a great, college which made my mom, happy.
Ⓒ I got into a great college, which made my mom happy.
Ⓓ I got into a great college which, made my mom happy.

7. **Choose the answer with the correct punctuation for the sentence below.**

Joyce remembered to bring her bathing suit on vacation but she left her sun screen in Dallas Texas.

Ⓐ Joyce remembered to bring her bathing suit on vacation, but she left her sun screen in Dallas, Texas.
Ⓑ Joyce remembered to bring her bathing suit on vacation but she left her sun screen in Dallas, Texas.
Ⓒ Joyce remembered to bring her bathing suit on vacation, but she left her sun screen in Dallas Texas.
Ⓓ Joyce remembered to bring her bathing suit, on vacation, but she left her sun screen, in Dallas, Texas.

8. **Choose the answer with the correct punctuation for the sentence below.**

Have you ever been to Albany New York, or Flourtown Pennsylvania.

Ⓐ Have you ever been to Albany, New York, or Flourtown Pennsylvania?
Ⓑ Have you ever been to Albany, New York or Flourtown, Pennsylvania.
Ⓒ Have you ever been to Albany New York, or Flourtown, Pennsylvania.
Ⓓ Have you ever been to Albany, New York or Flourtown, Pennsylvania?

9. Choose the answer with the correct punctuation for the sentence below.

Ryan stated "you shouldnt bully other kids.

   Ⓐ Ryan stated, you shouldn't bully other kids.
   Ⓑ Ryan stated, "you shouldnt bully other kids"
   Ⓒ Ryan stated, "you shouldnt bully other kids.
   Ⓓ Ryan stated, "You shouldn't bully other kids."

10. Choose the answer with the correct punctuation for the sentence below.

Michelle made pizza grilled cheese and tacos for lunch but she didnt realize it was only 10:00 a.m.

   Ⓐ Michelle made pizza, grilled, cheese, and tacos for lunch but she didnt realize that it was only 10:00 a.m.
   Ⓑ Michelle made pizza, grilled cheese, and tacos for lunch, but she didnt realize, it was only 10:00 a.m.
   Ⓒ Michelle made pizza, grilled cheese, and tacos for lunch, but she didn't realize it was only 10:00 a.m.
   Ⓓ Michelle made pizza, grilled, cheese, and tacos for lunch, but she didn't realize, it was only 10:00 am.

Chapter 2

Lesson 20: Correct Spelling

1. Choose the correct word that fits the blank:

Grind the wheat to a powdery _____.

Ⓐ flower
Ⓑ flour
Ⓒ floor
Ⓓ floure

2. Choose the correct word that fits the blank:

Among all _____, my favorite is the pink rose.

Ⓐ floors
Ⓑ flour
Ⓒ flowers
Ⓓ floures

3. Choose the correct word that fits the blank:

The last _____ creaked as I stepped on to it.

Ⓐ stare
Ⓑ stair
Ⓒ steer
Ⓓ stiar

4. Choose the correct word that fits in the blank:

He _____ the ball and it flew forward.

Ⓐ through
Ⓑ threw
Ⓒ throw
Ⓓ any of the above

5. Choose the answer with the correct set of words, in the given order, to fill in the blanks in the sentence below.

I am _____ fed up by all the noise in the city, and hence am heading to the countryside for some peace and _____.

Ⓐ quiet, quite
Ⓑ quite, quiet
Ⓒ quite, quite
Ⓓ quiet, quiet

6. Choose the correctly spelt word to fill in the blank in the sentence below.

Britney _____ a car for her 18th birthday.

Ⓐ received
Ⓑ recieved
Ⓒ purschesed
Ⓓ baught

7. Choose the correctly spelt word to fill in the blank in the sentence below.

The boy was very _____ about King Tut and Egypt.

Ⓐ nowledgeable
Ⓑ knowlegeable
Ⓒ knowledgeable
Ⓓ knoledgable

8. Choose the correctly spelt word to fill in the blank in the sentence below.

The black and white cat had really long _____.

Ⓐ whiskers
Ⓑ whisckers
Ⓒ wisikers
Ⓓ None of the above

9. **Choose the correctly spelt word to fill in the blank in the sentence below.**

My favorite_____ is a small Italian place on Elm Street.

Ⓐ restrant
Ⓑ resturannt
Ⓒ restaurant
Ⓓ restraent

10. **Choose the correctly spelt word to fill in the blank in the sentence below.**

The _____ of the school gave a student detention.

Ⓐ principle
Ⓑ princapal
Ⓒ principel
Ⓓ principal

Chapter 2

Lesson 21: Use Grade Appropriate Words

1. The word "racket" has multiple meanings.

   Which sentence uses the word "racket" where it means "noise?"

   Ⓐ I nearly forgot my racket before tennis practice.
   Ⓑ There was a lot of racket coming from my brother's room.
   Ⓒ My racket broke when I dropped it down the stairs.
   Ⓓ I hope I get a new racket for my birthday.

2. The word "bear" has multiple meanings.

   Which sentence uses the word "bear" where it means "to hold up?"

   Ⓐ The baby bear is so cute!
   Ⓑ I cannot bear to see someone hurt.
   Ⓒ That apple tree sure does bear a lot of fruit.
   Ⓓ I can't bear to stand on my broken ankle.

3. The word "patient" has multiple meanings.

   Which sentence uses the word "patient" where it means "quietly waiting?"

   Ⓐ The doctor sent the patient for x-rays of her wrist.
   Ⓑ The nurse checked on the patient frequently.
   Ⓒ The little boy is being very patient in line.
   Ⓓ The patient needs to go home and rest before he feels better.

4. The word "pound" has multiple meanings.

   Which sentence uses the word "pound" where it means "to hit?"

   Ⓐ We got our new dog from the pound.
   Ⓑ Jimmy had to pound on the box to get it to break open.
   Ⓒ The watermelon weighs 16 pounds!
   Ⓓ Sixteen ounces is equal to one pound.

5. The word "pack" has multiple meanings.

    Which sentence uses the word "pack" where it means "a group of animals?"

    Ⓐ Did you see that pack of wolves down in the valley?
    Ⓑ Don't forget to pack your toothbrush.
    Ⓒ I packed a sandwich, an apple, and a cookie in your lunch.
    Ⓓ Marissa put her pack on her back.

6. **Which of the following words best complete the sentence?**

    Even though I studied, I feel very _____ about the test in Science.

    Ⓐ excited
    Ⓑ anxious
    Ⓒ happy
    Ⓓ ready

7. **Which of the following words best completes the sentence?**

    I can't believe how _____ the Grand Canyon is.

    Ⓐ immense
    Ⓑ small
    Ⓒ brown
    Ⓓ stationary

8. **Which of the following words best completes the sentence?**

    They say the race is very _____, so I had better spend some extra time training.

    Ⓐ easy
    Ⓑ smooth
    Ⓒ distinct
    Ⓓ rigorous

9. **Which of the following words best completes the sentence?**

    Joey got himself into quite a _____ when he cheated on the test.

    Ⓐ predicament
    Ⓑ problem
    Ⓒ challenge
    Ⓓ bit of luck

10. Which of the following words best completes the sentence?

The team was very _____ about practicing.

Ⓐ lazy
Ⓑ sloppy
Ⓒ successful
Ⓓ diligent

Answer Key and Detailed Explanations

Chapter 2: Developing and Sustaining Foundational Language Skills

Lesson 1: Speaking & Listening

NOTE:

This lesson is an audio-visual lesson and is available online for your practice. Please use the link or QR code given below to practice the lesson. If you don't have an account, please register.

Have lots of fun!

Link	QR Code
http://lumoslearning.com/a/180818	

Lesson 2: Use Clues To Determine Multiple-meaning Words

Question No.	Answer	Detailed Explanations
1	C	According to the passage, crabs and shrimp are crustaceans. That is specifically said in the passage.
2	A	An exoskeleton is a skeleton outside the body, so the answer is A.
3	B	Bio means life, so a biopolymer is a substance found in living things.
4	A	This is a figurative expression and is not to be taken literally. Answer choice A is correct. It means they have more projects coming.
5	B	Smelly has a negative connotation; fragrant is positive. Based on what the paragraph says, these smell good.
6	B	Attracted and accepted do not mean the same thing as housed. Held means that they were in that branch, so that's the same meaning as housed.
7	C	The definition of brake that is used in this sentence is answer choice C.
8	B	Alive and dead are the only opposites listed in the above answer choices, so the correct answer is B.
9	D	If the volume of traffic was high, that means there was a lot of traffic on the interstate. The correct answer is D.
10	C	If you are earning something, that means it is an extra amount, so the answer is C.

Lesson 3: Interpret Figures Of Speech

Question No.	Answer	Detailed Explanations
1	D	The sentence uses the repeated sound /j/ so it is an example of alliteration and a comparison using "like" so it is also an example of a simile.
2	A	The sentence does not mean to literally not spill the beans but rather not tell a secret. The correct answer is A, idiom.
3	B	The sentence is comparing a sandwich to a car using "as" which means it is a simile.
4	A	An extreme exaggeration is an example of hyperbole.
5	C	The sentence is giving human like characteristics to a bear. This is personification.
6	D	A word that represents its sound is onomatopoeia.
7	B	The sentence is comparing Katy to a pig without using "like" or "as." This is a metaphor.
8	B	An extreme exaggeration is an example of hyperbole.
9	A	"Stop pulling my leg" does not mean that someone is literally pulling one's leg. It means to stop teasing. This is an idiom.
10	B	The sentence compares Danielle's dancing to a swan using "as." It is a simile.

Lesson 4: Use Context Clue To Determine Word Meaning

Question No.	Answer	Detailed Explanations
1	B	Julio was happy, not disappointed, but the text tells us that he was also something else. Satisfied and pleased are very similar to happy, so they are not something else. He expected other boys to win the title, so the best use of context to figure out the word "astounded" is to select "very surprised."
2	C	The signal word "but" tells us that the opposite of flimsy is strong because spider silk is stronger than steel.
3	A	The text tells us what is on every side of New Jersey, so we know that bordered is the same thing as surrounded by.
4	A	Answer A is the answer that makes the most sense. Africa is large, so none of the other answers make sense.
5	A	Never leaving someone means that you are loyal. Answer choice A is correct.
6	C	Based on the sentence, beneficial means good for you. Doctors wouldn't tell you to do it unless it was good for you.
7	D	Because it was unbearable, we know that the smell was awful. The correct answer is D.
8	A	Because the celebrity was overwhelmed, we know there were a lot of questions. For that reason, the answer is A.
9	C	Because it was summer, we know that sweltering means hot. It would never be cold on a beach in the summer.
10	A	We know that it will be a word with a negative connotation, and the only negative word that fits the sentence is A.

Lesson 5: Use Common Roots And Affixes

Question No.	Answer	Detailed Explanations
1	D	An affix can either be a prefix or a suffix, but a suffix will never be at the beginning of a word. Suffixes are only at the ends of words. The correct answer is D.
2	A	Incapable and not being able to do something are the same thing, so the only possible answer is A.
3	C	"-age" is the suffix that is the same in all three words. The correct answer is C.
4	B	"An-" is the only prefix that all three words have in common. The correct answer is B.
5	C	"Less" means "without," so the answer is C.
6	A	"-Ology" is the study of, so the answer is A. Although option D mentions study, -ology is not only the study of animals.
7	C	"Comm-" means "together," so C is the correct answer.
8	C	Both A and B are true, so the answer is C.
9	B	This is a two syllable word, so there should only be one hyphen between the n and the t. The answer is B.
10	D	Monarch only has two syllables, so it will only have one hyphen when you divide it. The hyphen should be between the two syllables, which is the case in answer choice D.

Lesson 6: Determine The Meaning Of A Word

Question No.	Answer	Detailed Explanations
1	B	Based upon the usage in the sentence, the word "misplaced" means to lose. The correct answer is B.
2	C	While the word "brisk" can mean both fast and cool, in this particular sentence it means "cool." The correct answer is C.
3	C	Since Natalie and Sophia are looking forward to their ride, the answer must have a positive connotation. The correct answer is "exciting," C.
4	D	Mundane means repetitive or boring. The correct answer choice is D. The context clues in the sentences help you determine this.
5	A	"Ravenous" means to be hungry. The correct answer is A. The context clues in the sentences help you determine this.
6	D	To triumph over someone or something means to win. The correct answer is D.
7	B	For something to be "bewitching" then it has captured your attention in a positive way. The correct answer is "charming," B.
8	D	Julia does not enjoy fishing, therefore it must be awful. The correct answer is D. The context clues in the sentences help you determine this.
9	A	In the context of the sentence, "perspective" means look or appearance. The correct answer is A.
10	D	A dictionary, thesaurus, and glossary can all give you an idea of what a word means. The correct answer is D, "All of the above."

Lesson 7: Use Relationships To Better Understand Words

Question No.	Answer	Detailed Explanations
1	A	The reason the flights were cancelled was the blizzard, so answer choice A is the only one that is correct.
2	B	The flood is what caused the people to be left homeless, so answer choice B is correct.
3	C	Pedro got the job because of his friendly attitude, so answer choice C is correct.
4	A	Answer choice A is correct because the only mammal listed is giraffe.
5	A	The only bird listed is a parrot, so A is correct.
6	B	The only dessert listed is pie, so B is the correct answer.
7	C	Answer choice C is the only one that puts things in the correct order.
8	B	Bees are the only insect listed, so answer choice B is correct.
9	B	The smoky smell was caused by the burned popcorn, so answer choice B is correct.
10	C	Answer choice C is the only one that shows the correct cause and effect.

Lesson 8: Maintain Consistency In Style And Tone

Question No.	Answer	Detailed Explanations
1	A	While each sentence says basically the same thing, only the first sentence paints the clearest picture of what was actually happening. The correct answer is A.
2	B	While each sentence has the same meaning, sentence B uses the most descriptive words and style.
3	D	Each sentence adds just a little more detail to better explain the topic. Answer choice D is correct.
4	B	Answer choice A appears to be too choppy while answer choice C is too short. The best answer choice is B.
5	D	Sometimes fewer words, and more to the point is best. The correct answer choice is D.
6	C	Even though there are still 2 sentences, answer choice C maintains the best style and tone for the sentences.
7	A	Choices A and D are both possible; however, answer choice A offers a more varied and imaginative sentence style.
8	B	Answer choice B has the best overall style and tone of the four choices.
9	B	While Beth thought the test was challenging, Mary thought it was easy.
10	C	Answer choice C uses the smoothest language while creating a picture of what is going on.

Lesson 9: Consult Reference Materials

Question No.	Answer	Detailed Explanations
1	B	Alphabetize means to rearrange the words in the order that they would appear in the dictionary. Answer choice B is the only one where the words are correctly alphabetized.
2	D	Alphabetize means to rearrange the words in the order that they would appear in the dictionary. Answer choice D is the only one where the words are alphabetized correctly.
3	D	Alphabetize means to rearrange the words in the order that they would appear in the dictionary. Answer choice D is the only one where the words are alphabetized correctly.
4	D	The dictionary contains all of these things, so answer choice D is true.
5	C	A synonym is what you find in the thesaurus. That is where you go when you're looking for a new word to replace an existing word.
6	B	Dictionaries are in alphabetical order, so answer choice B is correct.
7	D	Guidewords are at the top and guide you in your search for the word. They allow you to figure out if the word you are looking up falls within the guidewords for that page.
8		Organized is 3 syllables.
9	C	Jacket is 2 syllables, so the answer is C.
10	B	It has 3 syllables, so answer choice B is correct.

Lesson 10: Recognize Variations In English

Question No.	Answer	Detailed Explanations
1	D	The sentence says that mom made cookies yesterday which means it happened in the past. Therefore, you need to find an answer that is written in the past tense. Answer choice B is future. Answer choices A, C, and D are all past but only D makes sense. The correct answer is D.
2	A	The word "went" tells us this sentence is written in past tense. The only answer that is in past tense and makes sense is A, "bought."
3	B	While they're sounds right, the correct word would actually be their as it shows possession. They're represents 'they are' and that would not make sense in the sentence. The correct answer is B.
4	A	This sentence references something that will happen in the future. Answer choice A, "will build" makes the most sense and references something that will happen in the future.
5	D	With this sentence, we are looking for a word that will go along with "they" because the garden belongs to someone which tells us that we want to find a possessive word. The best answer choice is D, "their."
6	B	The answer choice that sounds the best is B, singing.
7	A	We are looking for a positive word that makes sense in the sentence. The best choice is A, "does."
8	D	Since Mickey's brother takes Mickey's toys we are looking for a pronoun to replace Mickey. The correct answer choice is D, his.
9	C	The sentence is referencing a specific group of holiday lights. In this case, the best choice is C, those.
10	D	The correct adverb to complete the sentence is happily, answer D.

Lesson 11: Distinguish Between Word Associations And Definitions

Question No.	Answer	Detailed Explanations
1	B	"Denotation" is the dictionary or literal meaning of a word. The correct answer is B.
2	C	"Connotation" refers to how the word makes us feel. The correct answer is C.
3	D	All the words listed have the same denotation as the word "house."
4	C	A child is often referred to as an adolescent. The correct answer is C.
5	C	Answer choices A and B, are structurally similar but the words have no similarities other than that. Answer choice D is opposites. Answer choice C is the correct answer.
6	D	Answer choice A and B are both antonyms so they do not have the same denotation. Horse and rabbits are similar in that they are both mammals but they do not have the same denotation. The correct answer is D.
7	D	The word "cheap" has a negative connotation to it.
8	B	The word Flop is not quite as hard as disaster therefore it has a positive connotation.
9	A	When thinking about something being messy, "filthy" is the answer choice that is the most negative.
10	C	A nice, or positive, way to say old is to say that someone is "elderly."

Lesson 12: Vary Sentence

Question No.	Answer	Detailed Explanations
1	D	The sentences can be combined to make a compound sentence using the conjunction so. The correct answer is D.
2	A	The sentences can be combined to make a compound sentence using the conjunction but. The correct answer is A.
3	C	The sentences can best be combined by listing the different things that will be at the party using commas to separate items in a series.
4	A	The sentence fragment, after school, can be used as a dependent clause to make a complex sentence. The correct answer is A.
5	D	To keep the sentences from being repetitive, they can be combined together. Answer choice D makes the most sense.
6	C	Since the author likes both summer and spring but spring best, it is best to combine these sentences into a compound sentence using the contrasting conjunction but.
7	B	The sentence fragment can be turned into a dependent clause to create a complex sentence. The correct answer is B.
8	C	Since the author is listing things they have to do, combining each task and separating them with commas is the best way to combine these sentences. The correct answer is C.
9	A	Combining the two sentences into one simple sentence is the best option. The correct answer is A.
10	B	Using the adjective brown to describe the puppy and listing its other attributes creates the best sentence. The correct answer is B.

Lesson 13: Correct Subject-verb Agreement

Question No.	Answer	Detailed Explanations
1	B	The subject is plural (Tracy and Gary), so there needs to be a plural verb (one with no "s" at the end.)
2	B	"All" is a plural subject, so you need a plural verb (one without an "s".)
3	B	The subject of the sentence is people, which is plural. That means the verb needs to be plural (which means that the verb does not have an "s".)
4	D	Answer choice D is correct. The other three do not sound right if you read them carefully.
5	B	B is the correct answer. If you read all of the answer choices carefully, B is the only one that sounds correct.
6	B	B is the correct answer. Some is the plural subject of the sentence, so you need a plural verb (one without an "s".) Seem is the only one that sounds correct.
7	A	"All" is the plural subject of the sentence, so you need a plural verb (one with no "s".) That is why A "appear" is the correct answer.
8	B	Answer choice B is correct. "Parents and students" is the plural subject, so you need a plural verb (which is "are").
9	C	Either is a singular subject, so you need a singular verb (which is "has".)
10	C	The correct answer is C. "There are things" is the way it should be read. If it was only one THING, then it would read "There is a thing."

Lesson 14: Correct Use Of Adjectives And Adverbs

Question No.	Answer	Detailed Explanations
1	A	The answer is A, colorful. Adjectives are words that describe nouns, and colorful describes the pages. Reading is a verb (with the helping verb was.) Pages and book are both nouns because they are things.
2	B	The answer is B. Adjectives are words that describe nouns, and beautiful describes the noun planet. Earth is a proper noun and both system and planet are nouns.
3	C	The correct answer is C. Alien and airship are both nouns and ran is a verb. Frightened is the only describing word.
4	A	The answer is A. Adverbs answer the questions how, how often, when, where, how much, or to what extent. "Quite" shows to what extent the mother was unhappy.
5	D	The answer is D. Adverbs answer the questions how, how often, when, where, how much, or to what extent. Utterly shows to what extent the man was tired.
6	C	The answer is C. Once you find the verb (which is answered), ask yourself, "How were all of the questions answered?" "They were answered correctly." That's how you find the adverb.
7	C	Adverbs answer the questions how, how often, when, where, how much, or to what extent. The correct answer is C, "politely." This tells us how the girl asked for her book.
8	D	The answer is D. "Polka dot" and "cold" are both adjectives (or describing words) that describe the nouns "umbrella" and "rain." Protected is a verb, so these are the only two choices for adjectives.
9	A	Adverbs answer the questions how, how often, when, where, how much, or to what extent. The answer is A, "soundly." This modifies the verb "slept" and tells us HOW the family slept.
10	D	Adverbs answer the questions how, how often, when, where, how much, or to what extent. The answer is D, "hardly." This tells us to what extent the printer works.

Lesson 15: Recognize Pronouns

Question No.	Answer	Detailed Explanations
1	B	Answer choice B is correct. "Myself" is a reflexive pronoun. None of the other answer choices sound correct.
2	B	The correct answer is B, "ourselves", because "we" is the subject. That tells us that it is more than one person and the author is included in the decorations.
3	B	Because "she" is used in the sentence, we know the answer is B "herself". The other three answers do not make sense in the sentence.
4	B	The correct answer is B. "A student" is the referent of the pronoun in the sentence. That's how we know to use "he or she has" in the blank. "You" does not make sense because its 2nd person, and "a student" is 3rd person. For that reason, it can't be A or C. "They" is 3rd person, but is referring to more than one person.
5	C	The correct answer is C. The referent of the pronoun is "players", so we know the pronoun should be plural. "Her", "its", and "his" are all singular pronouns.
6	A	They mention that Carol is his friend, so we know that Sue is his girlfriend. The answer is A.
7	B	It mentions that riding without a helmet is a risk. We know from that, what the risk is. The answer is B.
8	B	The tragedy mentioned (the cat eating the goldfish) is what was terrible, so the answer is B.
9	D	Since it says Johnny is taller than Ahmed, then we know they are talking about how much Johnny has grown. The correct answer is D.
10	A	The Sharks and Jets performed great dances, so they is appropriate. The answer is A.

Lesson 16: Recognize And Correct Vague Pronouns

Question No.	Answer	Detailed Explanations
1	A	The antecedent in the sentence is HE, which is singular, therefore the correct pronoun would be his. The correct answer is A.
2	B	The antecedent in the sentence is students, which is plural, therefore the correct pronoun would be their. No other pronoun makes sense. The correct answer is B
3	D	The antecedent in the sentence is Gavin, which is a single boy, therefore the correct pronoun would be him. The correct answer is D.
4	A	The antecedents in the sentence are Emily and Nathan. Since there are two of them, the correct pronoun needs to be plural. The correct answer is A, they.
5	A	The antecedent in the sentence is students, which is plural, therefore the correct pronoun would be their. There would not be correct because it is not the correct use of the word. No other pronouns make sense. The correct answer is A.
6	B	The antecedent in the sentence is Roger. Since Roger is a single boy, the correct pronoun would be B, his.
7	C	The antecedent in the sentence is cookies, which is plural. Hence, the only pronoun which makes sense is them. The correct answer is C.
8	A	The antecedent in the sentence is store, which is singular. The correct pronoun would be its. No other pronoun makes sense. The correct answer is A.
9	B	The antecedent in the sentence is Patty. Since Patty is a singular girl, the correct pronoun is she. The correct answer is B.
10	D	The antecedents in the story are Billy and Luis. Since there are two of them, the pronoun should represent two individuals not one. The only pronoun that correctly completes the sentence is D, their.

Lesson 17: Recognize And Correct Shifts In Pronoun Number And Person

Question No.	Answer	Detailed Explanations
1	A	Since each student is singular, his/her will be the correct answer. Hence, choice A is correct.
2	B	While we know that her is a pronoun for girl, D is still not the correct answer choice because the sentence references girls (plural) and her is a singular pronoun. The does not fit in the sentence. There is the incorrect homophone choice. Answer choice B is the correct answer.
3	D	Since we know that Coach Bob is a boy and is singular, the correct answer would be D, his
4	A	The only answer choice that is grammatically correct is A, I. "Billy and me," does not sound right, nor does "Billy and us" or "Billy and his."
5	C	Since the sentence is talking about Mrs. Marshall's students, which is a collective grouping of students, we need to look for an answer choice which is plural. The best answer choice is C, "they."
6	D	Since Johnny is a boy, we need to find an answer that is in line with his gender. The best choice is answer D, "him."
7	A	Since Lucy is a girl, we know we are looking for a pronoun that represents a girl. The correct answer is A, "her."
8	C	When talking about Aunt Sara, the sentence says "my" which means one. Therefore, answer choices A and D will not work because they are both plurals. "He" isn't quite right because we don't know who he is. The correct answer choice is C, "I."
9	A	Since Tiffany is a girl, we are looking for an answer that supports this. "Her" doesn't sound right, so "she," answer A, is the correct answer.
10	C	The sentence talks about one dog who likes playing catch with his ball, therefore we are looking for a pronoun that is singular and male. The correct answer is C, "he."

Lesson 18: Demonstrate Command Of Capitalization

Question No.	Answer	Detailed Explanations
1	B	Answer choice B is correct. The beginning of the sentence should be capitalized. Also the city and state should be capitalized.
2	A	The correct answer is A. "My should be capitalized because it's the beginning of the sentence. "Doctor Billings" should be capitalized because that's his name. Saturday should be capitalized because it's one of the days of the week.
3	C	Answer choice C is correct. "Mother" should be capitalized because it is the beginning of the sentence. "Santa Maria" should be capitalized because it's a proper noun, the name of a place. "Doctor" should not be capitalized because it's not the name of a specific doctor.
4	D	"The" should be capitalized because it's the beginning of the sentence, but "principal" should not be capitalized. If it were "Principal Phillips" then it would be capitalized, because it would be a specific principal. "Pablo" should be capitalized because it's a person's name. The words "safety patrol" and "captain" should not be capitalized because they're not proper nouns.
5	A	Answer choice A is correct. "Captain Jones" is the name of a specific captain, so it should be capitalized. "American Legion" is a proper noun, and so is "Martin Luther King Jr. Elementary School." Therefore, they should both be capitalized.
6	D	Dad is the only proper noun in the sentence which needs to be capitalized.
7	B	Answer choice B is correct. The proper nouns are "Mom", "Angela", and "Friday".
8	C	Answer choice C is correct. "My" should be capitalized because it's the beginning of the sentence. German should be capitalized because it is a nationality, even though it is talking about a type of cake. Sunday should be capitalized because it is the day of the week.
9	A	Answer choice A is correct. "Kathy Barrett" should be capitalized because it's a name. "Stanley Street" is the name of the street, and "Dominos" is the name of the restaurant.
10	B	Answer choice B is correct. "Michael" should be capitalized because it's a name. "The Call and Wild" is capitalized because it's a title and "July" should be capitalized because it's one of the months of the year.

Lesson 19: Demonstrate Command Of Punctuation

Question No.	Answer	Detailed Explanations
1	A	You must have quotations around what is said out loud. For that reason, answer choice A is correct.
2	C	Answer choice C is correct. There are two comma rules in place here. There needs to be a comma in items in a series (bananas, oranges, and cherries) and there is a compound sentence, so there needs to be a comma before the but.
3	A	Answer choice A is correct. There needs to be a semicolon after year because there are two complete sentences. You can't just put them together with a comma. It has to be a comma and a conjunction or a semicolon.
4	C	Answer choice C is correct. There has to be quotation marks around anything that is said out loud.
5	B	The only comma should be between the day and year. An apostrophe is used in Year's because year is a singular day.
6	C	The correct answer is C. The only comma that is needed is between the two clauses. "Which made my mom happy" is a dependent clause and the other clause is independent. It needs a conjunction or to be set apart in commas.
7	A	The correct answer is A. This is a compound sentence, so there needs to be a comma between vacation and but. Also, there needs to be a comma between the city and state (Dallas, Texas.)
8	D	There must always be a comma between the city and state. There should be a comma after Albany and a comma after Flourtown. Since the sentence is a question, it should end with a question mark rather than a period.
9	D	Answer choice D is correct because it's the only one where the You is capitalized. Any time a new sentence is used in dialogue, the first word in the sentence needs to be capitalized. There should also be an apostrophe in the contraction shouldn't.
10	C	Answer choice C is correct. There should be commas in the items in a series (pizza, grilled cheese, and tacos) and there should be a comma before but (because it's a compound sentence.) There should also be an apostrophe in the word didn't because it is a contraction for the words did not.

Lesson 20: Correct Spelling

Question No.	Answer	Detailed Explanations
1	B	Answer choice B is correct because that is the correct spelling of the flour that you cook with. This type of flour is made from grinding wheat.
2	C	Answer choice C is the correct word for the type of flowers mentioned in the sentence. The other options do not make sense in the sentence.
3	B	Answer choice B is correct. Stair is the correct spelling as the word is used in the sentence. Option A is a homophone. Option C is another word for guiding.
4	B	Threw is the correct word to use in the above sentence. The others are homophones.
5	B	The first word is an adverb meaning "very," and the second word is an adjective meaning "not loud."
6	A	Answer choice A has the correct spelling of the word. Options C and D make sense but are not spelled correctly.
7	C	Answer choice C has the correct spelling of the word.
8	A	Answer choice A has the correct spelling of the word.
9	C	Answer choice C has the correct spelling of the word.
10	D	Answer choice D has the correct spelling of principal as it is used in the sentence. Option A is spelled correctly, but the definition does not make sense in the sentence.

Lesson 21: Use Grade Appropriate Words

Question No.	Answer	Detailed Explanations
1	B	Answer choice B is an example of the word racket when it means noise.
2	D	In answer choice D, since the person has to bear weight or hold themselves up on their broken ankle, it is the correct answer.
3	C	If the little boy is being patient in line then he is quietly waiting. The correct answer is C.
4	B	Pounding on something until it breaks would be pounding to hit. The correct answer is B.
5	A	A pack or group of wolves mean that answer choice A is correct.
6	B	Since the author uses the words "even though they studied" it gives the impression that they did not feel too confident about their test. This would mean they felt anxious. The correct answer choice is B.
7	A	While the Grand Canyon is brown and stationary it is not small. The best word to describe it would be immense. The correct answer is A.
8	D	If a person needs to spend extra time training for a race then it probably is not easy or smooth. The correct answer choice is D, rigorous.
9	A	If Joey got caught cheating then he probably got himself into a predicament. The correct answer is A.
10	D	The best thing a team could be would be diligent about practicing. The correct answer choice is D.

Chapter 3

Comprehension Skills

Chapter 3

Lesson 1: Determine Technical Meanings

1. **What is a synonym of a word?**

   Ⓐ A word that has the same meaning as the given word.
   Ⓑ A word that has the opposite meaning of a given word.
   Ⓒ A word that has the same spelling as the given word.
   Ⓓ A word that has the same pronunciation as the given word.

2. **Which of the following statements is true about antonyms?**

   Ⓐ They have the same meaning as the given word.
   Ⓑ They are the definitions of a given word.
   Ⓒ They have the same sounds as a given word.
   Ⓓ They are the opposites of a given word.

The words "minute" (time) and "minute" (extremely small) are pronounced differently and have different meanings.

3. **These types of words are called _____.**

   Ⓐ Homophones
   Ⓑ Homonyms
   Ⓒ Homographs
   Ⓓ Homo-words

4. **Which of the choices below is an example of an "antonym?"**

   Ⓐ Clever, crazy
   Ⓑ Pretty, beautiful
   Ⓒ Narrow, skinny
   Ⓓ Abundant, scarce

5. **Which of the choices below is an example of synonyms?**

   Ⓐ mini, tiny
   Ⓑ clever, foolish
   Ⓒ good, bad
   Ⓓ soggy, dry

6. **Choose the correct set of antonyms from the following.**

   Ⓐ courteous, kind
   Ⓑ regretted, refused
   Ⓒ brief, small
   Ⓓ stopped, started

7. **Choose the set of rhyming words from the following.**

   Ⓐ fresh, air
   Ⓑ space, spread
   Ⓒ worms, germs
   Ⓓ breathe, breath

8. **A group of words that share the same spelling and pronunciation but have different meanings is called a _____.**

   Ⓐ Synonym
   Ⓑ Homonym
   Ⓒ Syllable
   Ⓓ Consonant

9. **Which of the following statements defines homophones?**

   Ⓐ The words that have the same meaning and different spellings.
   Ⓑ The words that have the same sound but different meanings.
   Ⓒ The words that have the same sound but have different meanings and spellings.
   Ⓓ The words that do not have the same sound but have the same meaning and spelling.

10. **Identify the correct set of homophones from the following.**

   Ⓐ mustard, mustered
   Ⓑ loan, lone
   Ⓒ lumbar, lumber
   Ⓓ both A and B

Chapter 3

Lesson 2: Connotative Words And Phrases

1. **Choose the best word to complete each sentence.**

   My friend is very careful about spending money. I admire that, so I call him _____.

   Ⓐ thrifty
   Ⓑ stingy
   Ⓒ miserly
   Ⓓ selfish

2. **Choose the best word to complete each sentence.**

   My friend is very careful about spending money. I don't like that trait, so I call him _____.

   Ⓐ thrifty
   Ⓑ stingy
   Ⓒ rude
   Ⓓ mean

3. **Choose the best word to complete each sentence.**

   I admire the man who jumped on the subway tracks to rescue a stranger. He was certainly _____.

   Ⓐ foolhardy
   Ⓑ undecided
   Ⓒ courageous
   Ⓓ stupid

Faster than fairies, faster than witches,
Bridges and houses, hedges and ditches,
And charging along like troops in a battle,
All through the meadows the horses and cattle,
All of the sights of the hill and the plain,
Fly as thick as driving rain,
And ever again, in the wink of an eye,
Painted stations whistle by.

Here is a child who clambers and scrambles,
All by himself and gathering brambles;
Here is a tramp who stands and gazes,
And there is the green for stringing the daisies;
Here is a cart run away in the road,
Lumping along with man and load;
And here is a mill and there is a river,
Each a glimpse and gone forever.

-- R. L. STEVENSON

4. **In the above poem what does the word "brambles" mean?**

    Ⓐ people
    Ⓑ crowds of people
    Ⓒ train stations
    Ⓓ prickly blueberry - and blackberry bushes

The girls on the playground were playing hopscotch. They all played together at recess every day. The new girl sat at the corner of the playground by herself, so one of the girls was _____ and asked her if she wanted to join them.

5. **Which word best completes the sentence?**

    Ⓐ Snotty
    Ⓑ Proud
    Ⓒ Friendly
    Ⓓ Clever

Micky and Janie live in a quiet neighborhood and are very sweet and polite. However, the husband and wife are upset by their noisy neighbors.

6. Which of the following represents what they might say to their neighbors?

    Ⓐ Hey! Keep quiet over there!
    Ⓑ Hello...would you mind keep the noise level down? We have sleeping children over here.
    Ⓒ How dare you make this much noise when we have sleeping children over here!
    Ⓓ If you don't get quiet in the next 5 minutes, we're calling the cops!

The first aid supplies that were brought after the hurricane were _____. Even after they came, the survivors of the hurricane kept looking for supplies.

7. Which word best completes the sentence?

    Ⓐ inadequate
    Ⓑ helpful
    Ⓒ tragic
    Ⓓ important

Skipping school can _____ your future.

8. What word best fits in the blank?

    Ⓐ effect
    Ⓑ help
    Ⓒ affect
    Ⓓ None of the above

The _____ candidate put his hands high in the sky and pumped his arms with a huge smile on his face.

9. What word best fits in the blank?

    Ⓐ unhappy
    Ⓑ bewildered
    Ⓒ victorious
    Ⓓ fun

Jackie read the newspaper and found out that there was a twister that hit Alabama and her heart broke for the affected families. The twister wiped out hundreds of houses. This was such a _____ event.

10. What word best fits in the blank?

Ⓐ exciting
Ⓑ tragic
Ⓒ unimportant
Ⓓ victorious

Chapter 3

Lesson 3: Meaning Of Words And Phrases

"That show made him a star overnight", said my friend about one of the actors. "He was completely unknown before. And now thousands of teenagers send him chocolates and love letters in the mail."

1. What does the above paragraph mean?

Ⓐ that the actor had poor acting skills
Ⓑ that the actor had come to fame recently
Ⓒ that nobody likes him now
Ⓓ none of the above

The forest's sentinel
Glides silently across the hill
And perches in an old pine tree,
A friendly presence his!
No harm can come
From night bird on the prowl.
His cry is mellow,
Much softer than a peacock's call.

Why then this fear of owls
Calling in the night?
If men must speak,
Then owls must hoot-
They have the right.
On me it casts no spell:
Rather, it seems to cry,
"The night is good- all's well, all's well."

-- RUSKIN BOND

2. What is the poet talking about in the first stanza?

Ⓐ how the owl comes out into the night
Ⓑ how the owl catches its prey
Ⓒ how the owl is looking into the dark night
Ⓓ how the owl walks

3. **What is the poet saying about the owl?**

Ⓐ He is comparing the owl to a sentinel
Ⓑ He is describing the flight of the owl
Ⓒ He is saying that the owl is friendly and harmless
Ⓓ All of the above

The sky was dark and overcast. It had been raining all night long, and there was no sign of it stopping. I thought that my Sunday would be ruined. As it poured outside, I settled down by the window to watch the rain. The park opposite my house looked even more green and fresh than usual. The branches of the tall trees swayed so hard in the strong wind that I thought they would break. A few children were splashing about in the mud puddles and having a wonderful time. I wished I could join them too! There were very few people out on the road and those who were hurried on their way, wrapped in raincoats and carrying umbrellas.

My mother announced that lunch was ready. It was piping hot and very welcoming in the damp weather. We spent the afternoon listening to music and to the downpour outside.

In the evening, we chatted and made paper boats that we meant to sail in the stream of water outside. It was not a bad day, after all!

4. **How does the writer end the passage?**

Ⓐ With a satisfied tone
Ⓑ With a sad tone
Ⓒ With an annoyed tone
Ⓓ With an excited tone

Androcles was a slave who escaped from his master and fled to the forest. As he was wandering there, he came upon a lion lying down moaning and groaning. Seeing the lion in pain, he removed a huge thorn from the beast's paw. After this incident, they lived together as great friends in the forest. Androcles was eventually arrested and condemned to death in the arena. He would be thrown to a lion that was captured and not given food for several days. The Emperor and his courtiers came to see the spectacle. Androcles was lead to the middle of the arena and so was the hungry lion. The lion roared and rushed towards its victim. But, as soon as he came near Androcles, he recognized him and licked his hands like a friendly dog. Everyone was surprised. The emperor heard the whole story and pardoned Androcles and freed the lion to his native forest.

5. **This story brings out the meaning of _____.**

Ⓐ Friendship
Ⓑ Slavery
Ⓒ Escape
Ⓓ Hunger

Last week, I fell off my bike and hurt myself badly. I bruised my elbow and sprained my wrist. My injuries would have been worse if I hadn't been wearing my bicycle helmet. My doctor asked me to tell this to all my friends so that they would wear helmets too. I told my teacher, and she asked me to make a public announcement during the school assembly. I had to talk about the accident and how the helmet protected me.

6. Why was I asked to tell everyone about my accident and mention wearing the helmet?

Ⓐ so that everyone understands the benefit of wearing a helmet
Ⓑ because it made an interesting story
Ⓒ so that everyone comes to know what a hero I am
Ⓓ so that helmets can be sold

Life and death were ideal as they crept into the dark world.

7. What is the mood of this sentence?

Ⓐ Ominous
Ⓑ Tragic
Ⓒ Dramatic
Ⓓ Silly

The man was feeble-minded and did not realize when others made fun of him by laughing at him and talking behind his back.

8. What is the tone of this sentence?

Ⓐ Unconcerned
Ⓑ Upsetting
Ⓒ Angry
Ⓓ Rude

My brother comes in my room and hides my dolls,
but my brother plays hide and seek with me.
My brother tells me I'm annoying and should leave his room,
but my brother stands up for me on the playground when someone is mean to me.
My brother plays with his friends and tells me I'm too young to join them,
but my brother plays with me in the snow when we have a snow day.

9. What is the hidden meaning in the poem?

Ⓐ The brother easily gets frustrated with his sibling.
Ⓑ The brother doesn't want to play with his sibling.
Ⓒ The brother really loves his sibling.
Ⓓ The brother likes to play with dolls.

Without you here, I can move forward
Thinking of the past only makes it worse,
Forgetting is the only way to continue on

10. What is the meaning of the poem?

Ⓐ The narrator is angry at someone
Ⓑ The narrator is moving away
Ⓒ The narrator wants to think of all the memories
Ⓓ The narrator wants to move forward; it is too sad to look back

Chapter 3

Lesson 4: Development Of Ideas

I always try to do what I have promised to do. If I say I will arrive at 5:15, I try to be there at 5:15. I don't lie or deliberately withhold information. I don't try to trick or confuse others. My friends trust me with their secrets, and I don't tell them to anyone else. I understand that you are looking for a trustworthy employee.

1. **Select the concluding sentence that most completely summarizes the argument in the passage.**

   Ⓐ If you are looking for an employee who doesn't lie, then you should hire me.
   Ⓑ If you are looking for an employee who needs to be at work at 5:15, then you should hire me.
   Ⓒ If you are looking for a trustworthy person, you should hire me.
   Ⓓ I believe I would make a very good employee and would love to be considered for a position at your company.

If I am chosen to be class president, I will represent you on the Student Council. I will listen to your requests and be sure that they are heard. I will show up for meetings. I will try to make our school a better place.

2. **Select the concluding sentence that most completely summarizes the argument in the passage.**

   Ⓐ If you vote for me, I will be a good class president.
   Ⓑ I am a good leader.
   Ⓒ I will work towards scrapping exams.
   Ⓓ The food in the cafeteria is awful.

Cats do not require as much attention as dogs. Dogs love you, and they want you to love them back. Cats are independent creatures. They don't need to be petted all the time. If you go on vacation for a few days, your dog may get lonely and refuse to eat, but your cat won't care.

3. **Select the concluding sentence that most completely summarizes the argument in the passage.**

   Ⓐ If you really want a pet, it would be a good idea to get a cat and a dog.
   Ⓑ If you don't have a lot of time to care for a pet, a dog is a better choice for you than a cat.
   Ⓒ Vacations are a good idea if you have a cat as a pet.
   Ⓓ If you don't have a lot of time to care for a pet, a cat is a better choice for you than a dog.

4. **Choose the best possible supporting detail to most accurately complete the statements.**

    1. The beach is a perfect place to take a vacation.
    2. I love to laze around on the sands.
    3. _____
    4. That is why I love to take a vacation at the beach.

    Ⓐ I love the smell of sea water.
    Ⓑ I hate the smell of sea water.
    Ⓒ Starfish are so cool.
    Ⓓ I like to see aircraft fly.

5. **Choose the best possible supporting detail to most accurately complete the statements.**

    1. Christmas is everybody's favorite holiday.
    2. One gets to do a lot of shopping.
    3. _____.
    4. That is why everybody loves Christmas.

    Ⓐ Christmas break is boring because you don't get to see your school friends every day.
    Ⓑ The school gives a lot of homework to do over the holidays.
    Ⓒ Decorating the Christmas tree is a lot of work.
    Ⓓ There's a spirit of giving.

One evening, long after most people had gone to bed, a friend and I were making our way merrily back home through the silent and almost deserted streets. We had been to a musical show and were talking about the actor we had seen and heard in it.

"That show made him a star overnight," said my friend about one of the actors. "He was completely unknown before, and now thousands of teenagers send him chocolates and love letters through the mail."

"I thought he was quite good," I said, "but not worth thousands of love letters daily. As a matter of fact, one of his songs gave me pain."

"What was that?" my friend asked. "Sing to me." I burst into a parody of the song.

"Be quiet for heaven's sake!" My friend gave me an astonished look. "You'll give everybody a fright and wake people up for miles around."

"Never mind," I said, intoxicated with the sound of my own voice. "I don't care. How does it matter?"

And I went on singing the latest tunes at the top of my voice.

Presently there came behind us the sound of heavy footsteps, and before I could say "Jack Robinson," a policeman was standing in front of me, his notebook open, and a determined look on his face.

"Excuse me, sir," he said. "You have a remarkable voice if I may say so. Who taught you to sing? I'd very much like to find someone who can give my daughter singing lessons. Would you be kind enough to tell me your name and address? Then my wife or I can drop you a line and discuss the matter."

6. Choose the best title for the above passage.

- Ⓐ The Singer
- Ⓑ A Pleasant Surprise
- Ⓒ The Musical Show
- Ⓓ The Policeman

The sky was dark and overcast. It had been raining all night long, and there was no sign of it stopping. I thought that my Sunday would be ruined. As it poured outside, I settled down by the window to watch the rain. The park opposite my house looked even more green and fresh than usual. The branches of the tall trees swayed so hard in the strong wind that I thought they would break. A few children were splashing about in the mud puddles and having a wonderful time. I wished I could join them too! There were very few people out on the road and those who were hurried on their way, wrapped in raincoats and carrying umbrellas.

My mother announced that lunch was ready. It was piping hot and very welcoming in the damp weather. We spent the afternoon listening to music and to the downpour outside.

In the evening, we chatted and made paper boats that we meant to sail in the stream of water outside. It was not a bad day, after all!

7. What detail in the above passage tells us that it was a cloudy day?

- Ⓐ The sky was dark and overcast.
- Ⓑ It had been raining all night long.
- Ⓒ A few children were splashing about in the mud puddles.
- Ⓓ The park opposite my house looked even more green and fresh.

The girls went to the park to play on the swings as they did each day. Their mothers always told them never to talk to strangers and always stick together. No one should walk home alone.

8. What message did the girls get from their mothers?

Ⓐ Stay together and stay away from strangers.
Ⓑ Only walk home alone if there is no one else to talk with you.
Ⓒ Be friendly to anyone you meet.
Ⓓ Enjoy the park and the people.

Suzanne and her brother always helped out at the shelter. They gave out food to people who would otherwise be hungry. They also gave out blankets, clothes, and jackets. Suzanne and her brother did this twice a month. When they gave these people food, blankets, clothes, and jackets, their faces lit up and they couldn't say thank you enough times.

9. Which statement indicates the primary message?

Ⓐ It is always nice and rewarding to help others.
Ⓑ Giving others blankets, clothes, and food can change their lives.
Ⓒ Giving people food will allow them to not go hungry.
Ⓓ Helping others always involves giving blankets.

Allison went to swim practice and worked very hard to try and perfect her flip turn. A flip turn is a turn where you flip underwater and turn to go back in the direction that you came from. Allison practiced 1 hour before school and 3 hours after school each day. On the weekends she practiced 5 hours a day! Allison thought she would never get the flip turn down right, but she practiced and practiced. Finally, after two weeks straight of practicing, she nailed it.

10. Which statement indicates the primary message?

Ⓐ If you practice less than two weeks, you won't accomplish your goal.
Ⓑ Only practice on the weekends.
Ⓒ Keep trying and don't give up.
Ⓓ Keep trying, but give up if you get too tired.

Chapter 3

Lesson 5: Analyze How People, Events, Or Ideas Are Presented In Text

Everywhere around us, there are millions of tiny living things called germs. They are so tiny that they can be seen only under the most powerful microscope. Some of these germs are no wider than twenty-five thousandths of an inch!

Louis Pasteur, the great French scientist, was the first to prove that germs exist. The germs in the air can be counted. The number of germs around us, especially in crowded rooms, is tremendous. Certain scientists counted 42,000 germs in approximately one cubic meter of air in a picture gallery when it was empty. But when the gallery was crowded with people, they found nearly 5,000,000 germs in the same place. In the open-air germs are less abundant. There are fewer germs in the country air than in town air. We see at once how important it is, therefore, to live as much as possible in the open air, and for the rooms, we live in to always be well ventilated by fresh air.

1. **What is the central idea of the above passage?**

    Ⓐ Louis Pasteur was a great French scientist.
    Ⓑ Germs are everywhere.
    Ⓒ Germs are small.
    Ⓓ Germs can be counted.

2. **Which of the following details does NOT support the central idea of the passage?**

    Ⓐ Germs are tiny and can only be seen using powerful microscopes.
    Ⓑ There are fewer germs in open air.
    Ⓒ The more people you are around, the sicker you will become.
    Ⓓ Germs are living things.

George Washington was the first and most popular U.S. President. He was the only one elected by a unanimous vote. It is often said of him that he was "first in war, first in peace, and first in the hearts of his countrymen."

Washington led comparatively untrained and ill-equipped American soldiers to victory over the well-trained British in the Revolutionary War. As soon as the Constitution was ratified, he was chosen to be President.

Many of the generals who had fought under Washington did not believe that the 13 colonies could cooperate to form a single country without the strong leadership of a king. They approached him, saying that they would support him as King George I of the United States. Washington was dismayed at the idea and asked the generals to promise never to mention it again. He served two terms as President and refused a third term, retiring to his farm in Virginia. When England's King George heard that Washington had voluntarily given up the power of the presidency, he said, "If that is true, he is the greatest man in history."

3. **What is the central idea of the above passage?**

   Ⓐ George Washington refused a third term as president.
   Ⓑ King George said that Washington is a great man.
   Ⓒ George Washington was also known as King George I of the United States.
   Ⓓ George Washington was a general and the first president of United States of America.

4. **Based upon the story about George Washington, which of the following words best describe him?**

   Ⓐ Smart
   Ⓑ Power hungry
   Ⓒ Strong leader
   Ⓓ Kind

When Michael Jordan played for the Chicago Bulls, they had one winning season after another. He scored more than 100 points in 1,108 games, won two Olympic gold medals and was ranked #1 by ESPN Magazine. Chosen for the NBA All-Stars 14 times, Jordan was ten times the scoring champ, five times the Most Valuable Player, and six times the scoring champ of the NBA. When he began losing his hair, he shaved his head completely and started a fashion trend for other players. He was chosen to make an animated movie called "Space Jam" with Bugs Bunny. No other player has come close to those achievements.

5. **Which of the following would be the best introductory, or topic sentence, for the above passage?**

   Ⓐ Michael Jordan is often considered to be the greatest basketball player of all time.
   Ⓑ Michael Jordan loves playing basketball.
   Ⓒ When Michael Jordan isn't playing basketball he is starring in movies.
   Ⓓ Michael Jordan won games, medals, and awards as a basketball player.

6. **Which of the following sentences best supports the central idea of the passage?**

   Ⓐ Michael Jordan was scoring champ of the NBA six times.
   Ⓑ Michael Jordan scored more than 100 points in 1,108 games.
   Ⓒ Michael Jordan is best friends with Bugs Bunny.
   Ⓓ Both A and B.

When Westinghouse, the inventor of the air brake, was working on his great invention, he made an application for a trial of his device to the New York Central Railroad. Vanderbilt, the president of the railroad, thought the inventor's claims were absurd. In comparison with the hand brake then in use, Westinghouse stated that one man instead of two could operate his brake and that his brake would stop a fifty-car train in fifty yards, compared to a sixty-five car train in two hundred yards with hand brakes.

It is said that Vanderbilt roared with laughter. The idea of stopping a train of cars by wind appeared to him to be a joke. So he returned the letter, with these words scribbled at the bottom: "I have no time to waste on fools."

The young inventor next turned to the head of another railroad. He was younger and more progressive than his New York rival. He sent for Westinghouse, listened to his explanations, and even advanced him money to continue his experiments. Best of all, he tested the new brake and found that Westinghouse was on the right track. Vanderbilt, hearing of the test, regretted his curt dismissal of the idea. He wrote a courteous note to the inventor, fixing a time for an interview. The note came back with the brief inscription: "I have no time to waste on fools," George Westinghouse.

7. What is the above passage mostly about?

Ⓐ Railroads during the 1800s
Ⓑ Vanderbilt and his dislike for fools
Ⓒ Air brakes
Ⓓ George Westinghouse's invention

8. How did Westinghouse react to Vanderbilt's dismissal of his idea?

Ⓐ Westinghouse gave up.
Ⓑ Westinghouse kept trying.
Ⓒ Westinghouse got mad at Vanderbilt.
Ⓓ Westinghouse decided to try inventing something else.

9. What kind of person does the passage illustrate George Westinghouse to be?

Ⓐ Foolish
Ⓑ Smart
Ⓒ Determined
Ⓓ Courteous

Books were hard to get for the mountain men among the western settlers. Sometimes a mountain man would carry a single battered book with him for years. Some of the men had Bibles, and even more had Shakespeare's plays. Shakespeare was a favorite with mountain men, even if they could not read. When they found someone who could read, he was often asked to read one of Shakespeare's plays to a group over a campfire. There were mountain men who could not sign their own names but could quote passages of Shakespeare by heart.

10. How does the author of the above passage show that books were important to mountain men?

Ⓐ Books were hard for mountain men to get.
Ⓑ Some mountain men had Shakespeare's plays.
Ⓒ Some mountain men could quote Shakespeare.
Ⓓ Not all mountain men could read.

Chapter 3

Lesson 6: Central Idea Of The Text

1. Books were hard to get for the mountain men among the western settlers.
2. Sometimes a mountain man would carry a single battered book with him for years.
3. Some of the men had Bibles, and even more had Shakespeare's plays.
4. Shakespeare was a favorite with mountain men, even if they could not read.
5. When they found someone who could read, he was often asked to read one of Shakespeare's plays to a group over a campfire.
6. There were mountain men who could not sign their own names but could quote passages of Shakespeare by heart.

1. **Which sentence best shows the central idea of this paragraph?**

   Ⓐ Sentence #1
   Ⓑ Sentence #6
   Ⓒ Sentence #3
   Ⓓ Sentence #5

2. **Which two sentences best support the central idea of the above paragraph?**

   Ⓐ Sentences #2 and #6
   Ⓑ Sentences #3 and #5
   Ⓒ Sentences #1 and #2
   Ⓓ Sentences #3 and #6

3. **Which sentence does not directly support the central idea?**

   Ⓐ Sentence #2
   Ⓑ Sentence #3
   Ⓒ Sentence #5
   Ⓓ Sentence #6

The rainforest has many layers. Different plants and animals live in each layer. Some layers get more sunlight than others.

4. **Which is the central idea of the passage?**

   Ⓐ We should take care of the rainforest.
   Ⓑ There are many layers in the rainforest.
   Ⓒ Some layers get sunlight.
   Ⓓ Rainforests are too wet.

5. **A main central idea is _____ and then has details that follow to support it.**

   Ⓐ specific
   Ⓑ general
   Ⓒ both specific and general
   Ⓓ very detailed

6. **The purpose of supporting details is _____.**

   Ⓐ to give you a conclusion
   Ⓑ to tell you the point of view of the story
   Ⓒ to tell the central idea
   Ⓓ to give more information to support the central idea

1. Homophones, homographs, and homonyms have different definitions.
2. Homophones are words that sound the same, but are spelled differently and have different meanings.
3. "The golfer drank tea before tee time."
4. Homographs are words that are spelled the same but are not pronounced the same way.
5. "The artist is planning to record a new record."
6. When two homographs are also homophones, they are called homonyms: word pairs that are spelled the same and pronounced the same way.
7. "He felt fine after he paid the fine."
8. "You can drink juice from a can."
9. You can remember homographs by remembering that "graph" means to write, as in autograph.
10. You can remember homophones by remembering that "phone" means sound, as in telephone.

7. **What is the author's probable purpose in including Sentences #9 and #10?**

   Ⓐ Sentences #9 and #10 help the reader remember the definition of homograph and homophone.
   Ⓑ Sentences #9 and #10 help the reader see the difference between a homograph and a homophone.
   Ⓒ Sentences #9 and #10 help the reader understand the definition of a homonym.
   Ⓓ Sentences #9 and #10 help the reader understand the difference between a homophone and a homonym.

8. **Which sentence is the central idea of the passage?**

   Ⓐ Sentence #1
   Ⓑ Sentence #4
   Ⓒ Sentence #6
   Ⓓ Sentence #10

9. **Which sentence is a supporting detail for Sentence #2?**

   Ⓐ Sentence #3
   Ⓑ Sentence #4
   Ⓒ Sentence #5
   Ⓓ Sentence #10

10. **What sentence is supported by detail in Sentence #7?**

   Ⓐ Sentence #8
   Ⓑ Sentence #6
   Ⓒ Sentence #7
   Ⓓ Sentence #5

Chapter 3

Lesson 7: Summary Of Text

One evening, long after most people had gone to bed, a friend and I were making our way merrily back home through the silent and almost deserted streets. We had been to a musical show and were talking about the actor we had seen and heard in it.

"That show made him a star overnight," said my friend about one of the actors. "He was completely unknown before, and now thousands of teenagers send him chocolates and love letters through the mail."

"I thought he was quite good," I said, "but not worth thousands of love letters daily. As a matter of fact, one of his songs gave me pain."

"What was that?" my friend asked. "Sing to me." I burst into a parody of the song.

"Be quiet for heaven's sake!" My friend gave me an astonished look. "You'll give everybody a fright and wake people up for miles around."

"Never mind," I said, intoxicated with the sound of my own voice. "I don't care. How does it matter?"

And I went on singing the latest tunes at the top of my voice.

Presently there came behind us the sound of heavy footsteps, and before I could say "Jack Robinson," a policeman was standing in front of me, his notebook open, and a determined look on his face.

"Excuse me, sir," he said. "You have a remarkable voice if I may say so. Who taught you to sing? I'd very much like to find someone who can give my daughter singing lessons. Would you be kind enough to tell me your name and address? Then my wife or I can drop you a line and discuss the matter."

1. **What probably happened at the end of the story?**

    Ⓐ Both the friends went home and had dinner
    Ⓑ The writer gave the policeman his name and address.
    Ⓒ The policeman arrested both the friends
    Ⓓ They went to see another musical show

Thomas is on the football team, the basketball team, and the hockey team. He even likes to run when he has free time.

2. By reading this you can conclude that _____?

Ⓐ Thomas does not like soccer.
Ⓑ Thomas is an athlete.
Ⓒ Thomas only likes sports that use a ball.
Ⓓ Thomas wishes he did not play that many sports.

Michael decided to climb a ladder to get his frisbee that landed on the roof. His father always told him to be careful when using a ladder because ladders were dangerous. Michael put on his bike helmet, asked his friend to hold the ladder, and put one hand in front of the other while climbing, never letting go of the ladder.

3. What can you conclude about climbing a ladder?

Ⓐ It is a lot of fun.
Ⓑ It is easy if you know what to do.
Ⓒ You should only climb a ladder if you are over 13 years old.
Ⓓ It can be very dangerous.

On the first day of school, there are many supplies that a student needs. Every student needs a notebook, pencils, pens, highlighters, and the most important, a calendar.

4. What sentence below most closely agrees with these sentences?

Ⓐ All of these items help a student stay organized throughout the year.
Ⓑ These items are only helpful for students who enjoy math.
Ⓒ These items are expensive, so only buy a few of them.
Ⓓ You may not need all these items to stay organized.

It is great to have a younger sibling. Some people may think it is annoying, but those people don't realize the benefits of having a younger sibling. First, a younger sibling can do your chores for you, so you don't get in trouble. Second, they can feed the animals, so you don't have to do that. Third, they can actually be fun to play with when you are stuck at home on a snow day.

5. What can you summarize from this passage?

Ⓐ It is great to have younger siblings.
Ⓑ Younger siblings are annoying.
Ⓒ You only want a sibling to be older than you.
Ⓓ Being an only child is the best.

Ryan earned money each week from doing chores around the house. His mother always told him that it was his money, but he should not spend it on useless things. Ryan decided to take $5.00 out of his piggy bank and went into the candy store. He looked at all the different types of candy and spent all of his $5.00.

6. **What is the most important message in this passage?**

   Ⓐ Ryan loves candy.
   Ⓑ Ryan begged for his money.
   Ⓒ Ryan had a green piggy bank.
   Ⓓ Ryan shared his candy with his friends.

The little girl got to pick out new furniture and decorate her room. She really liked the white bed and dresser. She decided to paint her walls pink and get a pink carpet. She was so excited to be getting a new room!

7. **What can you summarize about this little girl?**

   Ⓐ She had always had a room to herself.
   Ⓑ She was excited to redo her room the way she wanted.
   Ⓒ She wanted to paint her room purple.
   Ⓓ Her mother wasn't happy with her decisions.

Damon was moving to another state on the other side of the country. Along the way as his family drove, they stopped in Illinois, Idaho, and South Dakota; none of the towns they stopped in were like his hometown. When he arrived in his new hometown, he was excited to be living in a different state.

8. **What can you summarize about this passage?**

   Ⓐ Damon was moving to South Dakota.
   Ⓑ Damon guessed that his new hometown would not be like his old hometown, but was excited to be moving anyway.
   Ⓒ Damon did not want to stop in other states along the way.
   Ⓓ Damon was moving to Illinois.

The girl stood looking out the window
No one was out there, not even an animal.
The wind blew softly and rain started to fall.
The clouds rolled in and the thunder came.
The girl felt like she was looking through the window into her own mood.

9. **Based on this poem, what answer best describes the girl's mood?**

   Ⓐ The girl liked to be alone.
   Ⓑ She was scared of the rain.
   Ⓒ The girl was sad and unhappy.
   Ⓓ The girl was excited.

A boy embarked on a journey
Not knowing where he would end up.
He packed his things and headed out West.
It took him days and days to get to where he was going.
He was nervous and scared about what may be out there.
When the boy arrived, he wasn't sure if he was ready for what was to come.

10. **What was the boy doing?**

   Ⓐ The boy was moving and starting a new life.
   Ⓑ The boy was going to become an actor.
   Ⓒ The boy was going to find his long lost brother.
   Ⓓ The boy was going on a vacation.

Chapter 3

Lesson 8: Evaluating Arguments In Text

Michael Jordan was the greatest basketball player of all time. He scored more than 100 points in 1,108 games, won two Olympic gold medals and was ranked #1 by ESPN Magazine. Chosen for the NBA All-Stars 14 times, Jordan was ten times the scoring champ, five times the Most Valuable Player, and six times the scoring champ of the NBA. No other player has come close to those achievements.

1. **Identify the central idea – the claim – in the above persuasive paragraph.** _____.

   Ⓐ Jordan was six times the 'scoring champ' for NBA.
   Ⓑ Jordan was chosen for the NBA All-Stars 14 times.
   Ⓒ Jordan was the greatest basketball player.
   Ⓓ Jordan was a basketball player.

Michael Jordan was the greatest basketball player of all time. When he played for the Chicago Bulls, they had one winning season after another. When he began losing his hair, he shaved his head completely and started a fashion trend for other players. He was chosen to make an animated movie called "Space Jam" with Bugs Bunny. There are many good players, but Michael Jordan will always be my favorite.

2. **The claim: Jordan was the greatest basketball player.**

   Detail to support this claim include:_____.

   Ⓐ He was the best player on the team.
   Ⓑ When he began losing his hair, he shaved his head completely and started a fashion trend for other players.
   Ⓒ He was chosen to make an animated movie called "Space Jam" with Bugs Bunny.
   Ⓓ When he played for the Chicago Bulls, they had one winning season after another.

Life in the city is always exciting. There are more than a million people in the city where I live. There are street fairs and sidewalk vendors downtown. Most days, people are going about their daily business, just working. In that way, a big city is no different from a small town. But, in the city, there are many more concerts, lectures, theatrical performances, and other kinds of entertainment. Most of those things are expensive, and I can't afford to go. Because of the curfew, young people aren't allowed on the streets at night, and I usually have a lot of homework.

3. **Why would I like to live in a city?**

   Select the answer with the best arguments to support the above sentence:

   Ⓐ 1. City life is always exciting.
       2. There are one million people living in the city.
   Ⓑ 1. There are street fairs and sidewalk vendors.
       2. There are concerts and all kinds of entertainment.
   Ⓒ 1. Young people aren't allowed on the streets at night.
       2. I have a lot of homework.
   Ⓓ 1. Most of the things are expensive.
       2. I can't afford to go to these exciting places.

4. **Why can't young people enjoy city life?**

   Select the answer with the best arguments to support the above sentence:

   Ⓐ 1. City life is always exciting.
       2. Too many people live in the city.
   Ⓑ 1. There are street fairs and sidewalk vendors.
       2. There are concerts and all kinds of entertainment.
   Ⓒ 1. There's a curfew for young people at night.
       2. Young people have no time due to too much homework.
   Ⓓ 1. People go about their daily work.
       2. A big city is actually no different from a small town.

Fast food is unhealthy; it leads to obesity and disease, but the convenience and addictiveness of it contribute to the laziness of the general population. Most people eat fast food because they lack time to prepare a more nutritious meal. It seems as though there is fast food restaurant on every street corner. The general population overlooks the fact that eating nothing but these greasy foods will contribute to weight gain. Fast food is addictive because it is easily accessible and tastes so good.

5. **In the above passage, which sentence supports the argument that fast food contributes to unhealthy weight gain?**

   Ⓐ Most people eat fast food because they lack time to prepare a more nutritious meal.
   Ⓑ It seems as though there is a fast-food restaurant on every street corner.
   Ⓒ The general population overlooks the fact that eating nothing but these greasy foods will cause you to gain weight.
   Ⓓ Fast food is addictive for the convenience of it.

Kickboxing is a great form of exercise. This type of exercise tones your entire body. Punching a bag helps you gain strength and muscle in your arms. You also use the bag to do different types of kicks, thus strengthening your legs as well. Kickboxing is a total body workout that everyone should try.

6. The claim: Kickboxing is a great form of exercise.

Select the answer that most completely supports the claim:_____

Ⓐ This exercise routine allows you to use a punching bag.
Ⓑ This exercise strengthens your muscles.
Ⓒ This type of exercise tones your entire body.
Ⓓ Kickboxing is the new trend in exercise routines.

Electric cars are a new, innovative type of car that help the environment. They use little to no gas, there by keeping pollutants out of the air. They may be a little more expensive than the average car, but you will make that money back in savings on gas. The electric car is now being made by almost all car companies.

7. The claim: Electric cars are a new, innovative type of car.

Detail to support the claim include: _____

Ⓐ Electric cars are a great way to help the environment.
Ⓑ Electric cars are only a few years old.
Ⓒ Electric cars are expensive.
Ⓓ Most companies are now making electric cars.

Running a marathon is a great accomplishment. Training for a marathon takes months. First, you have to start running short distances and increase the distance you run each week. During your training, you will eventually start running 20 miles at a time. A full marathon is 26.2 miles and very hard for people to finish. With a little time, training, and hard work, anyone can run a marathon. Completing the marathon is a great accomplishment because it shows excellent dedication and athletic ability.

8. Identify the claim in this passage.

Ⓐ Running a marathon requires you to train a lot.
Ⓑ Running a marathon is a great accomplishment.
Ⓒ Running requires excellent dedication.
Ⓓ Not many people are able to complete a marathon.

Smartphones are the newest innovative technology out there. On the smartphone, you can video chat with your friends or family members to keep in touch. Smartphones also are a great way to stay organized and keep your life on track. Smartphones are an easy way to search the internet when you are out and need to find something quickly. They allow you to access tons of information.

9. Which sentence is the claim of the passage?

Ⓐ Smart phones are the newest innovative technology out there.
Ⓑ Smart phones are the best phone out there.
Ⓒ Smart phones are the best way to stay organized.
Ⓓ Smart phones can be used for video chatting.

Horses are used for many different types of activities. Horses can be used to pull carts. They are also used for riding English style in which the rider can jump and show them. Horses can also be used for riding Western-style in which riders can herd and rope cattle and go on trail rides. An English-style rider can also perform dressage, which is a highly precise series of movements involving the rider and the horse.

10. Identify the claim in this paragraph.

Ⓐ Dressage is the most intricate form of horse training.
Ⓑ Horses can be used for many different activities.
Ⓒ Horses can be ridden English style.
Ⓓ Horses can be ridden Western style.

Chapter 3

Lesson 9: Characters Responses And Changes

One evening, long after most people had gone to bed, a friend and I were making our way merrily back home through the silent and almost deserted streets. We had been to a musical show and were talking about the actor we had seen and heard in it.

"That show made him a star overnight," said my friend about one of the actors. "He was completely unknown before, and now thousands of teenagers send him chocolates and love letters through the mail."

"I thought he was quite good," I said, "but not worth thousands of love letters daily. As a matter of fact, one of his songs gave me pain."

"Which was that?" my friend asked. "Sing to me." I burst into a parody of the song.

"Be quiet for heaven's sake!" My friend gave me an astonished look. "You'll give everybody a fright and wake people up for miles around."

"Never mind," I said, intoxicated with the sound of my own voice. "I don't care. Why does it matter?"

And I went on singing the latest tunes at the top of my voice. Presently there came behind us the sound of heavy footsteps, and before I could say "Jack Robinson," a policeman was standing in front of me, his notebook open, and a determined look on his face.

"Excuse me, sir," he said. "You have a remarkable voice if I may say so. Who taught you to sing? I'd very much like to find someone who can give my daughter singing lessons. Would you be kind enough to tell me your name and address? Then my wife or I can drop you a line and discuss the matter."

1. **Who are the three characters in the above passage?**

   Ⓐ the writer, the writer's friend, and the actor
   Ⓑ the writer, the writer's friend, and the singer
   Ⓒ the neighbors, the policeman, and his friend
   Ⓓ the writer, the writer's friend, and the policeman

2. **Who were the writer and his friend referring to when they were talking and said "his songs"?**

   Ⓐ their neighbors
   Ⓑ the policeman
   Ⓒ the actor who sang in the musical show
   Ⓓ the friend

The sky was dark and overcast. It had been raining all night long, and there was no sign of it stopping. I thought that my Sunday would be ruined. As it poured outside, I settled down by the window to watch the rain. The park opposite my house looked even more green and fresh than usual. The branches of the tall trees swayed so hard in the strong wind that I thought they would break. A few children were splashing about in the mud puddles and having a wonderful time. I wished I could join them too! There were very few people out on the road and those who were hurried on their way, wrapped in raincoats and carrying umbrellas.

My mother announced that lunch was ready. It was piping hot and very welcoming in the damp weather. We spent the afternoon listening to music and to the downpour outside.

In the evening, we chatted and made paper boats that we meant to sail in the stream of water outside. It was not a bad day, after all!

3. **Who is the main character in the above passage?**

   Ⓐ The rain
   Ⓑ The writer's mom
   Ⓒ The writer
   Ⓓ The wind

4. **The character in a story who dominates is a _____.**

   Ⓐ minor character
   Ⓑ major character
   Ⓒ supporting character
   Ⓓ Joker

Sally woke up earlier than she expected one morning. Something wasn't right. She then realized what had awakened her. It was an unfamiliar sound. She listened closely and realized that the sound was coming from outside. Climbing out of her bed, she slipped into her robe and slippers and went to the window. Looking out, she soon spotted a small kitten under the tree that stood outside her window. She stood, staring at the helpless creature. It didn't move. It soon spotted her and meowed, as if it were calling out to her.

Sally left her room and found her mother in the kitchen. She excitedly told her mom about the kitten. "I am going outside to get the poor little thing," she told her mother.

"I'll go with you," her mom replied. Together they walked into the backyard. The kitten was still there waiting for them. Sally picked it up in her arms. The little kitten felt so soft and cuddly. She had always wanted a kitten and wondered if her mother would allow her to keep him. Her mother decided to first feed the kitten. She also decided to make a few calls to see where he came from. The kitten certainly needed a home. Sally became more hopeful that she would be able to keep the kitten.

5. The characters in the story are _____.

    Ⓐ the kitten
    Ⓑ the mother
    Ⓒ Sally
    Ⓓ All of the above

6. The main character in a story is usually known as the _____.

    Ⓐ Protagonist
    Ⓑ Antagonist
    Ⓒ One who saves everyone
    Ⓓ The one who messes everything up

7. The descriptions given by an author about the character's personality, habits, likes and dislikes are called?

    Ⓐ Character style
    Ⓑ Character flaws
    Ⓒ Character traits
    Ⓓ Character ideas

Having to start at a new school didn't worry Jane at all; she was ready for anything.

8. A character trait of Jane is _____.

    Ⓐ Easy-going
    Ⓑ Shy
    Ⓒ Scared
    Ⓓ Nervous

Realizing his son's dog was still in the burning building, the dad ran back into the building.

9. A character trait of the father is _____.

    Ⓐ Nervous
    Ⓑ Scared
    Ⓒ Carefree
    Ⓓ Selfless

Ever since Greg was little, he always liked to take things apart. He took apart his sister's dolls, took apart all his trucks and cars, and even took apart his parents' telephone to see how it worked.

10. A character trait of Greg is_____?

   Ⓐ Destructive
   Ⓑ Angry
   Ⓒ Curious
   Ⓓ Mean

Chapter 3

Lesson 10: Develop Setting

The sky was dark and overcast. It had been raining all night long, and there was no sign of it stopping. I thought that my Sunday would be ruined. As it poured outside, I settled down by the window to watch the rain. The park opposite my house looked even more green and fresh than usual. The branches of the tall trees swayed so hard in the strong wind that I thought they would break. A few children were splashing about in the mud puddles and having a wonderful time. I wished I could join them too! There were very few people out on the road and those who were hurried on their way, wrapped in raincoats and carrying umbrellas.

My mother announced that lunch was ready. It was piping hot and very welcoming in the damp weather. We spent the afternoon listening to music and to the downpour outside.

In the evening, we chatted and made paper boats that we meant to sail in the stream of water outside. It was not a bad day, after all!

1. **What is the setting of the above story?**

   Ⓐ The home of the writer
   Ⓑ The park
   Ⓒ The writer's village
   Ⓓ The writer's office

One evening, long after most people had gone to bed, a friend and I were making our way merrily back home through the silent and almost deserted streets. We had been to a musical show and were talking about the actor we had seen and heard in it.

"That show made him a star overnight," said my friend about one of the actors. "He was completely unknown before, and now thousands of teenagers send him chocolates and love letters through the mail."

"I thought he was quite good," I said, "but not worth thousands of love letters daily. As a matter of fact, one of his songs gave me pain."

"Which was that?" my friend asked. "Sing to me." I burst into a parody of the song.

"Be quiet for heaven's sake!" My friend gave me an astonished look. "You'll give everybody a fright and wake people up for miles around."

"Never mind," I said, intoxicated with the sound of my own voice. "I don't care. How does it matter?"

And I went on singing the latest tunes at the top of my voice. Presently there came behind us the sound of heavy footsteps, and before I could say "Jack Robinson," a policeman was standing in front of me, his notebook open, and a determined look on his face.

"Excuse me, sir," he said. "You have a remarkable voice if I may say so. Who taught you to sing? I'd very much like to find someone who can give my daughter singing lessons. Would you be kind enough to tell me your name and address? Then my wife or I can drop you a line and discuss the matter."

2. **What detail in the above story tells us that it took place late in the night?**

   Ⓐ We had been to a musical show
   Ⓑ "Be quiet for heaven's sake."
   Ⓒ One evening, long after most people had gone to bed
   Ⓓ And I went on singing the latest tunes at the top of my voice

Sally woke up earlier than she expected one morning. Something wasn't right. She then realized what had awakened her. It was an unfamiliar sound. She listened closely and realized that the sound was coming from outside. Climbing out of her bed, she slipped into her robe and slippers and went to the window. Looking out, she soon spotted a small kitten under the tree that stood outside her window. She stood, staring at the helpless creature. It didn't move. It soon spotted her and meowed, as if it were calling out to her.

Sally left her room and found her mother in the kitchen having her morning cup of coffee. She excitedly told her mom about the kitten. "I am going outside to get the poor little thing," she told her mother.

"I'll go with you," her mom replied. Together they walked into the backyard. The kitten was still there waiting for them. Sally picked it up in her arms. The little kitten felt so soft and cuddly in her arms. She had always wanted a kitten and wondered if her mother would allow her to keep him. Her mother decided to first feed the kitten. She also decided to make a few calls to see where he came from. The kitten certainly needed a home. Sally became more hopeful that she would be able to keep the kitten.

3. **What sentence(s) point(s) out the time of the story?**

   Ⓐ Sally went out of her room and found her mother in the kitchen having her morning cup of coffee.
   Ⓑ Sally went out of her room and found her mother in the kitchen.
   Ⓒ Sally woke up earlier than she expected one morning.
   Ⓓ Both A and C

4. From the story, we come to know that Sally lived _____.

     Ⓐ in a multi-storied building
     Ⓑ in a downtown, urban area
     Ⓒ in a motel
     Ⓓ in a single family house with a backyard

The forest's sentinel
Glides silently across the hill
And perches in an old pine tree,
A friendly presence his!
No harm can come
From night bird on the prowl.
His cry is mellow,
Much softer than a peacock's call.

Why then this fear of owls
Calling in the night?
If men must speak,
Then owls must hoot-
They have the right.
On me it casts no spell:
Rather, it seems to cry,
"The night is good- all's well, all's well."

-- RUSKIN BOND

5. The setting of this poem is in a _____.

     Ⓐ Sports stadium
     Ⓑ Forest
     Ⓒ House
     Ⓓ Palace

6. What is the setting of a story?

     Ⓐ Who and where the story takes place
     Ⓑ When and where the story takes place
     Ⓒ When and why the story takes place
     Ⓓ How and where the story takes place

Ralphie lived in the oldest and largest house on the block. Ralphie's friends were scared to visit him because of how worn down his house looked. The outside of the house was gray with cracks in the stucco and lots of spider webs hanging off it.

7.   What is the setting of the story?

Ⓐ Inside Ralphie's house
Ⓑ Inside Ralphie's friends' houses
Ⓒ Outside Ralphie's house
Ⓓ None of the above

The thieves intended to rob the bank around dinner time. They figured most people would be home eating with their families, so it would be easy for them to get in and out of the big green and gold bank.

8.   What is the setting of the story?

Ⓐ The bank on Green Street
Ⓑ The bank on Green Street at 7 pm
Ⓒ The green and gold bank at dinner time
Ⓓ The green and gold bank in the morning

Janice had her last final exam of the year; she was very excited and wanted to celebrate. After this final, she would no longer be a high school student.

9.   In what month was it most likely this last exam occurred?

Ⓐ In April
Ⓑ In June
Ⓒ In September
Ⓓ In December

Noah was excited that he got to share his birthday with his aunt. They were both born on the same day, just nineteen years apart. Their birthday was on April 13th.

10. In what season is Noah's birthday?

Ⓐ In the spring
Ⓑ In the summer
Ⓒ In the winter
Ⓓ In the fall

Chapter 3

Lesson 11: Analysis Of Key Events And Ideas

As it poured outside, I settled down by the window to watch the rain. The green park opposite my house looked even more green and fresh than usual. Strong winds shook the branches of the tall trees. Some of the branches swayed so hard in the strong winds that I thought they would break.

1. Why is the author using such clear descriptions?

    Ⓐ just to say that it was raining hard
    Ⓑ creating imagery to show the reader what that moment was like
    Ⓒ to tell us that the wind was blowing
    Ⓓ to explain what the trees look like when it rains

The Forest's Sentinel

At night, when all is still
The forest's sentinel
Glides silently across the hill
And perches in an old pine tree,
A friendly presence his!
No harm can come
From night bird on the prowl.
His cry is mellow,
Much softer than a peacock's call.
Why then this fear of owls
Calling in the night?
If men must speak,
Then owls must hoot-
They have the right.
On me it casts no spell:
Rather, it seems to cry,
"The night is good- all's well, all's well."
-- RUSKIN BOND

2. From what point of view is the above poem?

    Ⓐ First person point of view - from the owl's perspective
    Ⓑ 3rd person point of view - from an unknown bystander or the author
    Ⓒ First person point of view - from another animal's perspective
    Ⓓ None of the above

3. **According to the above poem when does the Owl come out?**

Ⓐ at night
Ⓑ at dawn
Ⓒ at dusk
Ⓓ at noon

Once upon a time, four boys lived in the countryside. One boy was very clever, but he did not like books. His name was Good Sense. The other boys were not very clever, but they read every book in the school. When they became grown men, they decided to go out into the world to earn their livelihood.

They left home and came to a forest where they halted for the night. When they woke up in the morning, they found the bones of a lion. Three of them, who had learned their books well at school, decided to make a lion out of the bones.

Good Sense told them, "A lion is a dangerous animal. It will kill us. Don't make a lion." But the three disregarded his advice and started making a lion. Good Sense was very clever. When his friends were busy making the lion, he climbed up a tree to save himself. No sooner had the three young men created the lion and gave it life, than it pounced upon them and ate them up. Good Sense climbed down the tree and went home very sadly.

4. **What did they see in the forest when they woke up in the morning?**

Ⓐ the bones of a lion
Ⓑ a witch that could bring an animal to life
Ⓒ Good Sense hiding in a tree
Ⓓ none of the above

5. **What did the four friends decide when they became grown men?**

Ⓐ They decided to go out into the world and earn their livelihood.
Ⓑ They decided to play with animal bones.
Ⓒ They decided to be friends forever.
Ⓓ They decided to never leave home.

6. **What advice did Good Sense give his friends?**

Ⓐ He told them how to create the lion.
Ⓑ He told them how to beat the lion once it was created.
Ⓒ He told them not to create the lion.
Ⓓ He told them to hide from the lion once they created it.

One evening, long after most people had gone to bed, a friend and I were making our way merrily back home through the silent and almost deserted streets. We had been to a musical show and were talking about the actor we had seen and heard in it.

"That show made him a star overnight," said my friend about one of the actors. "He was completely unknown before, and now thousands of teenagers send him chocolates and love letters through the mail."

"I thought he was quite good," I said, "but not worth thousands of love letters daily. As a matter of fact, one of his songs gave me pain."

"What was that?" my friend asked. "Sing to me." I burst into a parody of the song.

"Be quiet for heaven's sake!" My friend gave me an astonished look. "You'll give everybody a fright and wake people for miles around."

"Never mind," I said, intoxicated with the sound of my own voice. "I don't care. Why does it matter?" And I went on singing the latest tunes at the top of my voice.

Suddenly, there came behind us the sound of heavy footsteps, and before I could say "Jack Robinson," a policeman was standing in front of me, his notebook open, and a determined look on his face.

"Excuse me, sir," he said. "You have a remarkable voice if I may say so. Who taught you to sing? I'd very much like to find someone who can give my daughter singing lessons. Would you be kind enough to tell me your name and address? Then my wife or I can drop you a line and discuss the matter."

7.   Why was the friend telling the singer to be quiet?

    Ⓐ He did not like the sound of the singer's voice.
    Ⓑ He was embarrassed.
    Ⓒ He was worried that it would wake people for miles around.
    Ⓓ Because the policeman told them to be quiet.

The sky was dark and overcast. It had been raining all night long, and there was no sign of it stopping.

I thought that my Sunday would be ruined. As it poured outside, I settled down by the window to watch the rain. The park opposite my house looked even more green and fresh than usual. The branches of the tall trees swayed so hard in the strong wind that I thought they would break. A few children were splashing about in the mud puddles and having a wonderful time. I wished I could join them too! There were very few people out on the road and those who were hurried on their way, wrapped in raincoats and carrying umbrellas.

My mother announced that lunch was ready. It was piping hot and very welcoming in the damp weather. We spent the afternoon listening to music and to the downpour outside.

In the evening, we chatted and made paper boats that we meant to sail in the stream of water outside. It was not a bad day, after all!

8. What detail in the above passage tells us that the writer yearned to play outside?

Ⓐ The park opposite my house looked even more green and fresh.
Ⓑ We spent the afternoon listening to music and to the downpour outside.
Ⓒ I wished I could join them too!
Ⓓ All of the above.

Faster than fairies, faster than witches,
Bridges and houses, hedges and ditches,
And charging along like troops in a battle,
All through the meadows the horses and cattle,
All of the sights of the hill and the plain,
Fly as thick as driving rain,
And ever again, in the wink of an eye,
Painted stations whistle by.

Here is a child who clambers and scrambles,
All by himself and gathering brambles;
Here is a tramp who stands and gazes,
And there is the green for stringing the daisies;
Here is a cart run away in the road,
Lumping along with man and load;
And here is a mill and there is a river,
Each a glimpse and gone forever.

-- R. L. STEVENSON

9. What detail in the above poem tells us that this poem is about the view from inside a train?

Ⓐ All of the sights of the hill and the plain, Fly as thick as driving rain
Ⓑ Faster than fairies, faster than witches, Bridges and houses, hedges and ditches,
Ⓒ And ever again, in the wink of an eye, Painted stations whistle by.
Ⓓ Here is a cart run away in the road

Excerpt from Arabian Nights, Aladdin

After these words, the magician drew a ring off his finger, and put it on one of Aladdin's, telling him that it was a preservative against all evil, while he should observe what he had prescribed to him. After this instruction he said: "Go down boldly, child, and we shall both be rich all our lives."

Aladdin jumped into the cave, descended the steps, and found the three halls just as the African magician had described. He went through them with all the precaution the fear of death could inspire; crossed the garden without stopping, took down the lamp from the niche, threw out the wick and the liquor, and, as the magician had desired, put it in his vestband. But as he came down from the terrace, he stopped in the garden to observe the fruit, which he only had a glimpse of in crossing it. All the trees were loaded with extraordinary fruit, of different colors on each tree. Some bore fruit entirely white, and some clear and transparent as crystal; some pale red, and others deeper; some green, blue, and purple, and others yellow: in short, there were fruits of all colors. The white were pearls; the clear and transparent, diamonds; the deep red, rubies; the green, emeralds; the blue, turquoises; the purple, amethysts; and those that were of yellow cast, sapphires. Aladdin was altogether ignorant of their worth, and would have preferred figs and grapes, or any other fruits. But though he took them only for colored glass of little value, yet he was so pleased with the variety of the colors, and the beauty and extraordinary size of the seeming fruit, that he resolved to gather some of every sort; and accordingly filled the two new purses his uncle had bought for him with his clothes. Some he wrapped up in the skirts of his vest, which was of silk, large and full, and he crammed his bosom as full as it could hold.

Aladdin, having thus loaded himself with riches, returned through the three halls with the same precaution, made all the haste he could, that he might not make his uncle wait, and soon arrived at the mouth of the cave, where the African magician expected him with the utmost impatience. As soon as Aladdin saw him, he cried out: "Pray, uncle, lend me your hand, to help me out." "Give me the lamp first," replied the magician; "it will be troublesome to you." "Indeed, uncle," answered Aladdin, "I cannot now; it is not troublesome to me: but I will as soon as I am up." The African magician was so obstinate, that he would have the lamp before he would help him up; and Aladdin, who had encumbered himself so much with his fruit that he could not well get at it, refused to give it to him till he was out of the cave. The African magician, provoked at this obstinate refusal, flew into a passion, threw a little of his incense into the fire, which he had taken care to keep in, and no sooner pronounced two magical words, than the stone which had closed the mouth of the cave moved into its place, with the earth over it in the same manner as it lay at the arrival of the magician and Aladdin.

10. What did the magician put on one of Aladdin's fingers? Write your answer in the box below.

```
⬭
```

Chapter 3

Lesson 12: Conclusions Drawn From The Text

Sarah's mother told her to carry an umbrella on that Thursday morning before she left home for school, but Sarah did not want to do that. She already had her backpack and a gift for her friend to take with her. She just did not think it was necessary.

1. What can you infer about Sarah?

Ⓐ She is stubborn and only wants to do things if they seem right to her.
Ⓑ She does not like her mother.
Ⓒ She doesn't like getting wet.
Ⓓ She is a very obedient child.

2. What can you infer about the weather on that Thursday morning?

Ⓐ It was raining.
Ⓑ It was snowing.
Ⓒ It was going to rain.
Ⓓ It was a warm day.

The boy returned home a little late from school. He threw his coat as he walked in. He walked past his parents without greeting them. He headed straight to his room, slamming the door after him. He threw himself face down on his bed and lay there.

3. How is he feeling?

Ⓐ very delighted
Ⓑ very disappointed
Ⓒ very scared
Ⓓ very excited

Katie called out to her mother. The aroma of freshly brewed coffee filled the air. The sizzling sound of frying eggs reached her ears as she glided down the stairs. Now she could smell toast and bacon too. She ran to the table and sank into her seat just as her mother walked in from the kitchen. She was ready for _____

4. How is he feeling?

Ⓐ Dinner
Ⓑ Lunch
Ⓒ Breakfast
Ⓓ Sleeping

John wanted to buy some candy at the store. When he got there he realized he forgot his money.

5. **What can you infer as the action that John could take that would have the most chance of succeeding?**

Ⓐ John asked the store owner if he could pay him back another day.
Ⓑ John asked the store owner if he could work for the candy.
Ⓒ John walked outside and looked on the ground to see if anyone dropped money.
Ⓓ John walked back home and got the money he forgot.

Once upon a time, four boys lived in the countryside. One boy was very clever, but he did not like books. His name was Good Sense. The other boys were not very clever, but they read every book in the school. When they became grown men, they decided to go out into the world to earn their livelihood.

They left home and came to a forest where they halted for the night. When they woke up in the morning, they found the bones of a lion. Three of them, who had learned their books well at school, decided to make a lion out of the bones.

Good Sense told them, "A lion is a dangerous animal. It will kill us. Don't make a lion." But the three disregarded his advice and started making a lion. Good Sense was very clever. When his friends were busy making the lion, he climbed up a tree to save himself. No sooner had the three young men created the lion and gave it life, than it pounced upon them and ate them up. Good Sense climbed down the tree and went home very sadly.

6. **Which of the following statement(s) is true about Good Sense?**

Ⓐ He was very clever
Ⓑ He did not like books
Ⓒ He did not like the other boys
Ⓓ Both A and B

It is recommended that people should exercise every day, particularly those who spend many hours doing sedentary activities like playing cards, reading, or playing video games.

7. **We can infer that when people are doing sedentary activities, they must be _____.**

Ⓐ Running
Ⓑ Talking
Ⓒ Sitting
Ⓓ Jumping

The sky was dark and overcast. It had been raining all night long, and there was no sign of it stopping. I thought that my Sunday would be ruined. As it poured outside, I settled down by the window to watch the rain. The park opposite my house looked even more green and fresh than usual. The branches of the tall trees swayed so hard in the strong wind that I thought they would break. A few children were splashing about in the mud puddles and having a wonderful time. I wished I could join them too! There were very few people out on the road and those who were hurried on their way, wrapped in raincoats and carrying umbrellas.

My mother announced that lunch was ready. It was piping hot and very welcoming in the damp weather. We spent the afternoon listening to music and to the downpour outside.

In the evening, we chatted and made paper boats that we meant to sail in the stream of water outside. It was not a bad day, after all!

8. **When did the event described in the passage occur?**

   Ⓐ On a very nice and sunny day.
   Ⓑ On a wintry day.
   Ⓒ On a hot day.
   Ⓓ On a rainy day.

One evening, long after most people had gone to bed, a friend and I were making our way merrily back home through the silent and almost deserted streets. We had been to a musical show and were talking about the actor we had seen and heard in it.

"That show made him a star overnight," said my friend about one of the actors. "He was completely unknown before, and now thousands of teenagers send him chocolates and love letters through the mail."

"I thought he was quite good," I said, "but not worth thousands of love letters daily. As a matter of fact, one of his songs gave me pain."

"What was that?" my friend asked. "Sing to me." I burst into a parody of the song.

"Be quiet for heaven's sake!" My friend gave me an astonished look. "You'll give everybody a fright and wake people up for miles around."

"Never mind," I said, intoxicated with the sound of my own voice. "I don't care. How does it matter?"

And I went on singing the latest tunes at the top of my voice.

Presently there came behind us the sound of heavy footsteps, and before I could say "Jack Robinson," a policeman was standing in front of me, his notebook open, and a determined look on his face.

"Excuse me, sir," he said. "You have a remarkable voice if I may say so. Who taught you to sing? I'd very much like to find someone who can give my daughter singing lessons. Would you be kind enough to tell me your name and address? Then my wife or I can drop you a line and discuss the matter."

9. **Which detail in the above paragraph tells us that the author of the above passage is a male?**

   Ⓐ "He was completely unknown before"
   Ⓑ "And I went on singing the latest tunes at the top of my voice"
   Ⓒ "Excuse me, sir," he said
   Ⓓ "You have a remarkable voice"

The boy and his dog were watching television when they heard a loud bang. There was a thunderstorm outside and the boy guessed that lightning must have hit something. The dog started to whimper and hid under the table.
You can guess that _____.

10. **Complete the sentence above.**

   Ⓐ the dog was scared of the television show.
   Ⓑ the dog was in trouble.
   Ⓒ the dog was scared of the thunderstorm.
   Ⓓ the dog needed to go outside.

Chapter 3

Lesson 13: Structure Of Text

1. **Identify where the underlined sentence below belongs in the paragraph.**

    <u>Start with the freshest bread you can find.</u>

    I will tell you how to make a perfect peanut butter sandwich.
    Take the two pieces of bread.
    Add a good-sized scoop of crunchy peanut butter, and be sure to spread it on both pieces of bread.
    Find a jar of your favorite jam.
    Use slightly less jam than peanut butter, and spread it on only one slice of bread.
    Put the two slices together and cut the sandwich in half. Enjoy.

    Ⓐ The missing sentence should be first.
    Ⓑ The missing sentence should be second.
    Ⓒ The missing sentence should be third.
    Ⓓ The missing sentence should be fourth.

2. **Identify where the underlined sentence below belongs in the paragraph.**

    <u>During the pre-competition phase, continue the aerobic training, but add strength training and sprints.</u>

    Training for tennis can be broken down into four phases.
    During the preparation phase, work on aerobic fitness with jogging, swimming, or cycling as you train heavily on the specifics of tennis.
    While competing, training can ease up except for the specifics of tennis.
    For several weeks after competition, rest from playing tennis but keep up your fitness by playing other sports.

    Ⓐ The missing sentence should be first.
    Ⓑ The missing sentence should be second.
    Ⓒ The missing sentence should be third.
    Ⓓ The missing sentence should be fourth.

3. **Identify where the underlined sentence below belongs in the paragraph.**

In French, the word means "rotten pot."

Today we have spray cans for freshening the air, but it's more fun to make a potpourri. Potpourris were originally made in France by creating a mixture of flower petals and leaves that was allowed to sit in a crock for months. Today, many people still like to make potpourris from herbs and flowers. You can make your own from herbs and flowers from the garden.

Ⓐ The missing sentence should be first.
Ⓑ The missing sentence should be second.
Ⓒ The missing sentence should be third.
Ⓓ The missing sentence should be fourth.

4. **Arrange the sentences below in the most logical order.**

1. On the front of each cap is a white horse.
2. The caps also have the motto, "They fear no difficulty."
3. Officers can be identified by the crimson sash worn over their shoulders.
4. The tallest men have high bearskin caps.
5. The British troops present a colorful appearance.
6. Crowds gather to watch the elegant soldiers parade by.

Ⓐ 6, 1, 2, 5, 4, 3
Ⓑ 5, 3, 4, 1, 2, 6
Ⓒ 5, 4, 3, 6, 1, 2
Ⓓ 1, 2, 3, 4, 5, 6

5. **Arrange the sentences in the most logical order.**

1. Most farm families raised geese, so goose feathers were plentiful.
2. Colonists also used the feathers of wild turkeys and hawks.
3. Crow feathers were harder to collect, but were considered the best for making fine lines.
4. Colonists often made their quill pens from goose feathers.

Ⓐ 4, 1, 2, 3
Ⓑ 1, 2, 3, 4
Ⓒ 3, 2, 1, 4
Ⓓ 2, 3, 1, 4

6. Arrange the sentences in the most logical order.

1. Later, European traders spread pineapple growing to Africa and the Pacific Islands, including Hawaii.
2. The name was later changed to pineapple.
3. The name may come from the Dutch word for pinecone, which is pi jnappel.
4. Christopher Columbus was the first European to taste what he called "Indian pinecones."

Ⓐ 4, 3, 2, 1
Ⓑ 4, 1, 3, 2
Ⓒ 1, 2, 3, 4
Ⓓ 3, 2, 1, 4

When Westinghouse, the inventor of the air brake, was working on his great invention, he made an application for a trial of his device to the New York Central Railroad. Vanderbilt, the president of the railroad, thought the inventor's claims were absurd. In comparison with the hand brake then in use, Westinghouse stated that one man instead of two could operate his brake and that his brake would stop a fifty-car train in fifty yards, compared to a sixty-five car train in two hundred yards with hand brakes.

It is said that Vanderbilt roared with laughter. The idea of stopping a train of cars by wind appeared to him to be a joke. So he returned the letter, with these words scribbled at the bottom: "I have no time to waste on fools."

The young inventor next turned to the head of another railroad. He was younger and more progressive than his New York rival. He sent for Westinghouse, listened to his explanations, and even advanced him money to continue his experiments. Best of all, he tested the new brake and found that Westinghouse was on the right track. Vanderbilt, hearing of the test, regretted his curt dismissal of the idea. He wrote a courteous note to the inventor, fixing a time for an interview. The note came back with the brief inscription: "I have no time to waste on fools," George Westinghouse.

7. What kind of a writing piece is the above passage?

Ⓐ A personal narrative
Ⓑ A persuasive essay
Ⓒ An informative/expository passage
Ⓓ A journal entry

8. Which of the following would turn the above passage into a personal narrative?

Ⓐ If the above passage was written by Westinghouse himself.
Ⓑ If the author was President Vanderbilt and he wrote about George Westinghouse.
Ⓒ If the author was a third person.
Ⓓ None of the above

9. **What are the main parts of an essay?**

    Ⓐ A topic title
    Ⓑ An introduction to the topic
    Ⓒ Details about the topic and a conclusion to the topic
    Ⓓ All of the above

10. **What are the parts of a business letter?**

    Ⓐ The heading, the inside address
    Ⓑ The greeting, the body
    Ⓒ The complimentary close, the signature line
    Ⓓ All of the above

Chapter 3

Lesson 14: Cite Textual Evidence

Everywhere around us, there are millions of tiny living things called germs. They are so tiny that they can be seen only under the most powerful microscope. Some of these germs are no wider than twenty-five thousandths of an inch!

Louis Pasteur, the great French scientist, was the first to prove that germs exist. The germs in the air can be counted. The number of germs around us, especially in crowded rooms, is tremendous. Certain scientists counted 42,000 germs in approximately one cubic meter of air in a picture gallery when it was empty. But when the gallery was crowded with people, they found nearly 5,000,000 germs in the same place. In the open-air, germs are less abundant. There are fewer germs in the country air than in town air. We see at once how important it is, therefore, to live as much as possible in the open air, and for the rooms, we live in to always be well ventilated by fresh air.

1. **According to the passage, where will you find more germs?**

    Ⓐ In crowded spaces
    Ⓑ In the country
    Ⓒ In hospitals
    Ⓓ In empty rooms

2. **Which of the following statements can be concluded after reading the passage?**

    Ⓐ Louis Pasteur liked counting germs.
    Ⓑ Germs are too small to be seen.
    Ⓒ People have germs.
    Ⓓ Fresher air has fewer germs.

George Washington was the first and most popular U.S. President. He was the only one elected by a unanimous vote. It is often said of him that he was "first in war, first in peace, and first in the hearts of his countrymen." Washington led comparatively untrained and ill-equipped American soldiers to victory over the well-trained British in the Revolutionary War. As soon as the Constitution was ratified, he was chosen to be president.

Many of the generals who had fought under Washington did not believe that the 13 colonies could cooperate to form a single country without the strong leadership of a king. They approached him, saying that they would support him as King George I of the United States. Washington was dismayed at the idea and asked the generals to promise never to mention it again. He served two terms as president and refused a third term, retiring to his farm in Virginia. When England's King George heard that Washington had voluntarily given up the power of the presidency, he said, "If that is true, he is the greatest man in history."

3. How does the author show that George Washington is a great man?

(A) He led untrained soldiers into battle.
(B) He was unanimously elected president.
(C) He voluntarily gave up the power of the presidency.
(D) All of the above.

4. Based upon the above story about George Washington, which of the following words best describe him?

(A) Smart
(B) Power hungry
(C) Strong leader
(D) Kind

5. According to the text, why was Washington considered the most popular president?

(A) King George I said, "He is the greatest man in history."
(B) He was elected president by a unanimous vote.
(C) He wanted to be a powerful man and king.
(D) He was the first president

When Westinghouse, the inventor of the air brake, was working on his great invention, he made an application for a trial of his device to the New York Central Railroad. Vanderbilt, the president of the railroad, thought the inventor's claims were absurd. In comparison with the hand brake then in use, Westinghouse stated that one man instead of two could operate his brake and that his brake would stop a fifty-car train in fifty yards, compared to a sixty-five car train in two hundred yards with hand brakes.

It is said that Vanderbilt roared with laughter. The idea of stopping a train of cars using airpower appeared to be a joke to him. So, he returned the letter, with these words scribbled at the bottom: "I have no time to waste on fools."

The young inventor next turned to the head of another railroad. He was younger and more progressive than his New York rival. He sent for Westinghouse, listened to his explanations, and even advanced him money to continue his experiments. Best of all, he tested the new brake and found that Westinghouse was on the right track. Vanderbilt, hearing of the test, regretted his curt dismissal of the idea. He wrote a courteous note to the inventor, fixing a time for an interview. The note came back with the brief inscription: "I have no time to waste on fools," George Westinghouse.

6. Which of the following statements can be concluded after reading the passage above?

Ⓐ Westinghouse was thankful Vanderbilt helped him.
Ⓑ Vanderbilt regretted not listening to Westinghouse's ideas.
Ⓒ Westinghouse was a successful train engineer.
Ⓓ Westinghouse's invention was foolish.

Michael Jordan was the greatest basketball player of all time. When he played for the Chicago Bulls, they had one winning season after another. He scored more than 100 points in 1,108 games, won two Olympic gold medals and was ranked #1 by ESPN Magazine. Chosen for the NBA All-Stars 14 times, Jordan was ten times the scoring champ, five times the Most Valuable Player, and six times the scoring champ of the NBA. When he began losing his hair, he shaved his head completely and started a fashion trend for other players. He was chosen to make an animated movie called "Space Jam" with Bugs Bunny. No other player has come close to those achievements.

7. According to the passage, which of the following is NOT a reason why Michael Jordan is considered the greatest basketball player of all time?

Ⓐ Michael Jordan shaved his head.
Ⓑ Michael Jordan won two gold medals in the Olympics.
Ⓒ Michael Jordan scored more than 100 points in 1,108 games.
Ⓓ Michael Jordan was the Most Valuable Player five times.

8. Why did the author write this passage about Michael Jordan?

Ⓐ To describe about how Michael Jordan made a movie with Bugs Bunny.
Ⓑ To show what a great basketball player Michael Jordan is.
Ⓒ To give readers Michael Jordan's life story.
Ⓓ To tell people what it is like to be a famous basketball player.

Most of the planets in our solar system have moons. Saturn has the most, with eighteen moons. Jupiter has sixteen; Uranus has fifteen. Earth has only one, but our moon has a big influence on the lives of humans on Earth. In ancient times, people believed that moonlight could affect people's brains. The Latin word for the moon was Luna. Words like "lunatic" and "looney" come from that idea. Many people still believe that more babies are born and more people die when the moon is full. Scientific studies that have been done to see whether the numbers of births and deaths actually increase when there is a full moon show that there is no increase. The gravitational pull of the moon affects the tides in the ocean but does not seem to affect the births and deaths of people. Does the full moon cause people to fall in love? That's another question!

9. **What, according to the passage, has a "looney" effect on people?**

    Ⓐ The tides
    Ⓑ Saturn
    Ⓒ Babies
    Ⓓ The moon

10. **After reading this passage, what inference can you make?**

    Ⓐ People believe the moon causes crazy things to happen.
    Ⓑ Moonlight from the Earth's moon is less powerful because we only have one moon.
    Ⓒ People believe that births, deaths, and love is not influenced by the moon.
    Ⓓ Earth's moon is bigger than Jupiter's.

Chapter 3

Lesson 15: Understanding Author's Purpose and Point of View

Dogs are better pets than cats for many reasons. Dogs are a man's best friend and can learn tricks. Dogs will get you things when you ask them to. Dogs will go walking or running with you to help keep you in shape. Dogs like to cuddle and protect their owners.

1. What is the purpose of the above passage?

Ⓐ To inform
Ⓑ To explain
Ⓒ To persuade
Ⓓ To entertain

If you invent a new word and enough people like it, you may find it in the dictionary. Dictionaries add new words as they come into common use. The fancy word for a brand-new word is "neologism." In 2011, the Merriam-Webster Collegiate Dictionary added some neologisms you probably know, such as "tweet," "fist bump," and "social media."

Some of the new words may not be so familiar.

- "Planking" is a game of lying face down, hands at your sides, in the most unusual place you can think of, and having your picture taken and posted on the internet.
- A "bromance" is a close friendship – but not a romance – between two men.
- A "robocall" is a call made automatically by a machine repeating a taped message.
- A "helicopter parent" is one who hovers over their children, becoming much too involved in their lives.
- And "crowdsourcing"? That's the way many people can each do a little bit of a very large project.

The country of Iceland, for example, is crowdsourcing a new constitution for their country, so if you have an idea about what they ought to include, you can go online and send them your suggestion.

At the same time, new words are being added, old words that are no longer widely recognized are dropped from the dictionary. This year, the dictionary deleted the words "growlery" (a room where you can go to complain) and "brabble" (another word for squabble). If you haven't heard those words before, you probably won't miss them!

2. What is the purpose of the passage above?

  Ⓐ To inform
  Ⓑ To explain
  Ⓒ To persuade
  Ⓓ To entertain

I will tell you how to make a perfect peanut butter sandwich. Start with the freshest bread you can find. Take two pieces of bread. Add a good-sized scoop of crunchy peanut butter, and be sure to spread it on both pieces of bread. Find a jar of your favorite jam. Use slightly less jam than peanut butter, and spread it on only one slice of bread. Put the two slices together and cut the sandwich in half. Enjoy.

3. What is the purpose of the passage above?

  Ⓐ To inform
  Ⓑ To explain
  Ⓒ To persuade
  Ⓓ To entertain

4. What point of view is the paragraph above told from?

  Ⓐ First person
  Ⓑ Second person
  Ⓒ Third person
  Ⓓ Fourth person

Everywhere around us, there are millions of tiny living things called germs. They are so tiny that they can be seen only under the most powerful microscope. Some of these germs are no wider than twenty-five thousandths of an inch! Louis Pasteur, the great French scientist, was the first to prove that germs exist. The germs in the air can

be counted. The number of germs around us, especially in crowded rooms, is tremendous. Certain scientists counted 42,000 germs in approximately one cubic meter of air in a picture gallery when it was empty. But when the gallery was crowded with people, they found nearly 5,000,000 germs in the same place. In the open-air, germs are less abundant. There are fewer germs in the country air than in town air. We see at once how important it is, therefore, to live as much as possible in the open air, and for the rooms, we live in to always be well ventilated by fresh air.

5. What is the purpose of the passage above?

  Ⓐ To inform
  Ⓑ To explain
  Ⓒ To persuade
  Ⓓ To entertain

Football is the most exciting sport. During a football game, two teams of eleven players battle to reach the end zone. During the game, the players try to catch or run with the ball without being tackled by the opposing team. Sometimes players jump over each other, break tackles, and run as fast as lightning. Football fans cheer extremely loud when their team reaches the end zone. There is never a dull moment in football.

6. What is the purpose of the passage above?

Ⓐ To convince readers to go to a football game.
Ⓑ To tell a story about what happened at a football game.
Ⓒ To explain to readers about what happens at a football game.
Ⓓ To help the reader understand why to never attend a football game.

Eating carrots, broccoli, and string beans are good for you. Making sure to have healthy vegetables in your diet is important. Some people think eating vegetables at one meal is good enough, but it isn't; you should eat vegetables at least 3 meals a day.

7. What is the purpose of the passage above?

Ⓐ To convince the reader to eat more vegetables.
Ⓑ To give information about different types of vegetables.
Ⓒ To tell about a cartoon where the characters are played by vegetables.
Ⓓ The help the reader understand there is nothing important about vegetables.

George Washington was the first and most popular U.S. President. He was the only one elected by a unanimous vote. It is often said of him that he was "first in war, first in peace, and first in the hearts of his countrymen." Washington led comparatively untrained and ill-equipped American soldiers to victory over the well-trained British in the Revolutionary War. As soon as the Constitution was ratified, he was chosen to be President.

Many of the generals who had fought under Washington did not believe that the 13 colonies could cooperate to form a single country without the strong leadership of a king. They approached him, saying that they would support him as King George I of the United States. Washington was dismayed at the idea and asked the generals to promise never to mention it again. He served two terms as President and refused a third term, retiring to his farm in Virginia. When England's King George heard that Washington had voluntarily given up the power of the presidency, he said, "If that is true, he is the greatest man in history."

8. How does the author show that George Washington is a great man?

Ⓐ He led untrained soldiers into battle.
Ⓑ He was unanimously elected president.
Ⓒ He voluntarily gave up the power of the presidency.
Ⓓ All of the above.

Michael Jordan was the greatest basketball player of all time. When he played for the Chicago Bulls, they had one winning season after another. He scored more than 100 points in 1,108 games, won two Olympic gold medals and was ranked #1 by ESPN Magazine. Chosen for the NBA All-Stars 14 times, Jordan was ten times the scoring champ, five times the Most Valuable Player, and six times the scoring champ of the NBA. When he began losing his hair, he shaved his head completely and started a fashion trend for other players. He was chosen to make an animated movie called "Space Jam" with Bugs Bunny. No other player has come close to those achievements.

9. **Why did the author write this passage about Michael Jordan?**

    Ⓐ To tell about how Michael Jordan made a movie with Bugs Bunny.
    Ⓑ To show what a great basketball player Michael Jordan is.
    Ⓒ To give readers Michael Jordan's life story.
    Ⓓ To tell people what it is like to be a famous basketball player.

Most of the planets in our solar system have moons. Saturn has the most, with eighteen moons. Jupiter has sixteen; Uranus has fifteen. Earth has only one, but our moon has a big influence on the lives of humans on earth. In ancient times, people believed that moonlight could affect people's brains. The Latin word for the moon was Luna. Words like "lunatic" and "looney" come from that idea. Many people still believe that more babies are born and more people die when the moon is full. Scientific studies that have been done to see whether the numbers of births and deaths actually increase when there is a full moon show that there is no increase. The gravitational pull of the moon affects the tides in the ocean but does not seem to affect the births and deaths of people. Does the full moon cause people to fall in love? That's another question!

10. **What point of view is the story above told from?**

    Ⓐ First person
    Ⓑ Second person
    Ⓒ Third person
    Ⓓ Fourth person

In the original version of the story "The Three Little Pigs," the wolf chases the pigs and says he will huff and puff and blow their houses down.

The following paragraph is a different interpretation.

I've always been misunderstood. I'm allergic to hay. I can't help it that when I'm near hay, I huff and I puff and I sometimes blow things down. No one has any reason to be afraid of me, but sometimes they are. What happened to those poor little pigs is sad, but it was their own fault.

11. Who is talking in this paragraph?

Ⓐ The pigs in the story "The Three Little Pigs."
Ⓑ The wolf in the story "The Three Little Pigs."
Ⓒ A 3rd person narrator
Ⓓ None of the above

12. How is the narrator's point of view different from the traditional one?

Ⓐ He claims that he had no intention of blowing down the pigs' houses or of eating them, but that his allergies were at fault.
Ⓑ He claims that he had no intention of blowing down the pigs' house, but wanted to eat them up.
Ⓒ He claims that he had no intention of blowing down the pigs' houses or of eating them, but he just wanted to scare them.
Ⓓ He claims that another wolf blew the pigs' houses down and blamed it on him.

13. Why does the narrator claim to have been misunderstood?

Ⓐ Because everyone has regarded him as a bully who wants to occupy weaker animals' houses
Ⓑ Because everyone has regarded him as a pig-killing villain when he had no such intention.
Ⓒ Because everyone has regarded him sick and allergy-ridden.
Ⓓ Because he is evil.

I was shaking like a leaf. My palms were sweaty and I was so nervous about my presentation.

14. What point of view is this from?

   Ⓐ Third person omniscient
   Ⓑ Second person
   Ⓒ First person
   Ⓓ Third person

Heather loved her new dog. She played with it every day and took it for walks. The dog became Heather's best friend, and they did everything together.

15. What point of view is this told in?

   Ⓐ First person
   Ⓑ Second person
   Ⓒ Third person
   Ⓓ None of the above

In the original version of "Little Red Riding Hood," Red is delivering food to her sick grandmother when she stumbles upon a wolf in the house.

The following is a different interpretation of "Little Red Riding Hood,"

I'd been after that wolf for a long time, but when I went into the woods that day to deliver a basket to my grandmother, I promised my mother that I wouldn't leave the path to go wolf-hunting, even if I got a clear shot. I even spoke politely to him and did exactly as my mother asked. But when I got to grandma's house, I found that he had eaten her! I was determined to get revenge. Thank goodness the woodcutter came along and did my job for me. I don't need to get into any trouble with my mother, but it really burns me up when people think I couldn't have handled the wolf by myself!

16. Who is talking in this passage?

   Ⓐ Red Riding Hood in the story "Little Red Riding Hood"
   Ⓑ The wolf in the story "Little Red Riding Hood"
   Ⓒ The mother in the story "Little Red Riding Hood"
   Ⓓ A narrator

17. How is the narrator's point of view different from the traditional one?

Ⓐ She is traditionally thought of as a brave girl who wanted to fight the wily wolf.
Ⓑ The narrator's point of view is not different from the traditional one.
Ⓒ She is traditionally thought of as an innocent child, in danger from the wily wolf.
Ⓓ She is thought of as a mean girl who hates wolfs.

18. Why does the narrator claim to have been misunderstood?

Ⓐ She wanted people to think that she is a brave girl.
Ⓑ People think she couldn't have defeated the wolf.
Ⓒ People think that she does not follow her mother's instructions.
Ⓓ Both A and B

The forest's sentinel
Glides silently across the hill
And perches in an old pine tree,
A friendly presence his!
No harm can come
From night bird on the prowl.
His cry is mellow,
Much softer than a peacock's call.

Why then this fear of owls
Calling in the night?
If men must speak,
Then owls must hoot-
They have the right.
On me it casts no spell:
Rather, it seems to cry,
"The night is good- all's well, all's well."

-- RUSKIN BOND

19. In the above poem the author says 'If men must speak, Then owls must hoot-They have the right.' What does he mean by this?

Ⓐ That people should hoot like owls.
Ⓑ That owls should talk like people.
Ⓒ That owls hoot for the same reasons people speak. This is the way owls communicate.
Ⓓ That owls do not have the right to talk.

20. Which of the following are usually written in the second person point of view?

(A) Instructions
(B) Self-help books
(C) Directions
(D) All of the above

Chapter 3

Lesson 16: Figurative Words And Phrases

1. Choose the sentence below that is closest in meaning to the figurative expression.

Edgar was dead to the world when we got home.

Ⓐ Edgar was asleep when we got home.
Ⓑ Edgar was not moving or breathing.
Ⓒ Edgar had a head injury and was unconscious.
Ⓓ Edgar was not at home.

2. Choose the sentence below that is closest in meaning to the figurative expression.

You'd better go home; you're in hot water.

Ⓐ You'd better go home; you're in trouble
Ⓑ You'd better go home; you'll find hot water there.
Ⓒ You'd better go home; you are sweating.
Ⓓ You'd better go home and drink hot water.

3. Choose the sentence below that is closest in meaning to the figurative expression.

He put all the papers in the circular file.

Ⓐ He put the papers in the wastebasket.
Ⓑ He rolled up all the papers.
Ⓒ He put the papers in the round file cabinet.
Ⓓ He put the papers on the circular table.

4. Choose the word below that completes the figurative expression.

He works like a _____.

Ⓐ Lion
Ⓑ Dog
Ⓒ Parrot
Ⓓ Cat

5. Choose the word below that completes the figurative expression.

He is as stubborn as a _____.

Ⓐ Mule
Ⓑ Cow
Ⓒ Baby
Ⓓ Ice

6. Choose the sentence below that is closest in meaning to the figurative expression.

The secretary had a mountain of paper work. _____.

Ⓐ The secretary was dealing with paper art
Ⓑ The secretary had a large amount of work
Ⓒ The secretary had to run around a lot
Ⓓ The secretary had to meet a lot of people

7. Complete the sentence below so that it is closest in meaning to the figurative expression.

His room is a train wreck. It is _____.

Ⓐ full of toy trains
Ⓑ well organized
Ⓒ a mess
Ⓓ well laid out

8. Complete the sentence below so that it is closest in meaning to the figurative expression.

He is a star. He _____.

Ⓐ he loves soccer
Ⓑ wants to be an astronomer
Ⓒ acts in films
Ⓓ is very good at what he does

9. Complete the sentence below so that it is closest in meaning to the figurative expression.

She is my rock. She always _____ me.

Ⓐ puts me down
Ⓑ leans on
Ⓒ criticizes
Ⓓ supports

10. Complete the sentence below so that it is closest in meaning to the figurative expression.

I feel like a million bucks. I am _____.

Ⓐ elated
Ⓑ happy
Ⓒ discontented
Ⓓ Both A & B

Answer Key and Detailed Explanations

Chapter 3: Comprehension Skills

Lesson 1: Determine Technical Meanings

Question No.	Answer	Detailed Explanations
1	A	Answer A is correct because synonyms will basically have the same definition as the original word they are representing.
2	D	The words will have completely opposite meanings, so the answer is D.
3	C	<u>homophone</u> - same pronunciation, spelled differently, different meanings. <u>homonyms</u> - same spelling, different meaning. <u>homographs</u> - spelled the same, not necessarily pronounced the same, and different meaning <u>homo-word</u> - not found in grammar, <u>minute</u> - time is pronounced with a short vowel i and the u sounds like a short vowel i. <u>minute</u> - small is pronounced with a long vowel i and a long vowel u. Hence, answer choice C is correct. These are homographs.
4	D	Answer choice D is correct because those two words are complete opposites.
5	A	Answer choice A contains the synonym. The other answer choices are antonyms.
6	D	Answer choice D is the only one that gives words with opposite meanings, or antonyms.
7	C	Worms and germs are an almost perfect rhyme, so the answer is C.
8	B	That is the exact definition of a homonym, so the answer is B.
9	C	Answer choice C is correct because that is the exact definition of a homophone.
10	D	Answer choices A and B both have words that sound the same but are spelled differently and have different meanings. For that reason, the correct answer is D.

Lesson 2: Connotative Words And Phrases

Question No.	Answer	Detailed Explanations
1	A	Thrifty means that you don't want to spend money unless you have to and you want to save as much as possible. Answer choice A is correct.
2	B	Because the author of this sentence admitted that he/she didn't like the trait, we know there is a negative spin on the part of the author. That's why the correct answer is B.
3	C	'Courageous' is the word with the positive connotation.
4	D	Brambles are prickly bushes or shrubs. It specifically says that he was "all by himself" so we know other people weren't around.
5	C	It was very nice for the girl to ask the new student to join in. C is the answer.
6	B	Because they are characterized as being "sweet and polite" we would assume their actions would be in line with that. Answer choices A and D are very rude and hateful. Answer choice B is more of the way a sweet and polite couple would react.
7	A	The fact that they had to keep looking for supplies tells us that there were not enough supplies. The correct answer is A.
8	C	Affect is the correct word for the verb in this sentence.
9	C	The positive connotation of the words in the sentence show us that the candidate won. That is why C is the correct answer
10	B	The answer is B. Tragic is the only negative word that works in this sentence.

Lesson 3: Meaning Of Words And Phrases

Question No.	Answer	Detailed Explanations
1	B	Answer choice B is correct. Based on the sentences, it is clear that the person being discussed has come to fame recently.
2	A	The first part of the poem is how the owl comes out of the tree into the forest at night. The correct answer is A.
3	D	The poet said all of the above things in the opening lines of the poem.
4	A	The author did not seem excited, but was definitely not negative (annoyed or sad.) The correct answer is A.
5	A	Because the man had helped the lion, the man's life was spared. Even though it is a human and an animal, it is a story of friendship. The correct answer is A.
6	A	The correct answer is A. The teacher asked the student to share the story so that maybe more kids would wear helmets.
7	A	Ominous is kind of creepy and spooky. That is definitely the mood here. The answer is A.
8	B	When you hear that statement, it makes you feel bad for that man. The answer choice that is correct is B.
9	C	Answer choice C is correct. Even though the brother isn't always nice to his sister, his actions show her that he loves her.
10	D	Answer choice D is correct based on the poem. The author talks about moving forward and forgetting.

Lesson 4: Development Of Ideas

Question No.	Answer	Detailed Explanations
1	D	The correct answer is D because it is a good ending sentence and sums up the point of the paragraph. A and B are too specific, and C is repetitive.
2	A	The only answer that is a concluding sentence is answer choice A. It mentions class president, which is the point of the article. The other three answers are specific details and do not sum up the passage.
3	D	Answer choice D is correct. It correctly summarizes the point of the article. The other three answers do not make sense if you read the passage carefully.
4	A	The correct answer is A. Loving the smell of sea water supports loving the beach as far as a vacation trip. Although there are starfish in the ocean and sometimes aircraft fly by, neither of those details support the main idea of the paragraph. The author would not like vacationing at the beach if he/she hated the smell of sea water, so B is not correct.
5	D	Answer choice D is correct. All of the statements about Christmas are positive, so this detail will be positive too. All of the other answer choices are negative.
6	B	While all of the titles make sense, the best title would be B, "A Pleasant Surprise." The character in the story was very pleasantly surprised that he was not in trouble with the policeman.
7	A	The correct answer is A. Although all of the answers are true statements, the only one that gives the detail of the sky being cloudy is saying it is "dark and overcast."
8	A	The correct answer is A. The mothers specifically told the girls to stay together and stay away from strangers. Answer choices B and C are opposite of what the mothers told their daughters.
9	A	Answer A is the correct choice. The primary message of the passage is that it is rewarding to help others. Although giving people food helps them not to go hungry, it is only one detail of the passage. There is no evidence to show receiving the items changes people's lives, and helping others does not always mean giving blankets.
10	C	The correct answer is C. Allison worked very hard and did not give up, and she eventually accomplished her goal. A is not correct because it will take people different amounts of time to accomplish what they set out to do. The key is to never give up. D is the opposite of what the passage is saying, and B is never mentioned.

Lesson 5: Analyze How People, Events, Or Ideas Are Presented In Text

Question No.	Answer	Detailed Explanations
1	B	Answer choices A, C, and D present minor details related to the bigger, overall topic that germs are everywhere. The correct answer is B.
2	C	Answer choice C is the only answer that is not even presented in the story; therefore it is not a supporting detail. The correct answer is C.
3	D	Answers A and B both provide supporting details. Answer choice C is a misinterpretation of the text. Answer choice D presents what the passage is about – George Washington was a great general and president.
4	C	The text implies that George Washington was not interested in being powerful; therefore Answer B would not be a correct choice. There is no evidence within the text that either supports or disputes that George Washington was a kind man. While his actions certainly showed that he was a smart man, the fact that George Washington was a strong leader is implied in how he led his army as well as knew when it was his time to share the power by leaving office.
5	A	The only answer choice which completely identifies who Michael Jordan is and why is answer choice A. This would make the best, broad introductory sentence.
6	D	Both answer choices A and B support the central idea of the passage that Michael Jordan is a great basketball player. Answer choice C does not support the central idea. The correct answer choice is D.
7	D	While the passage does talk about the railroads, Vanderbilt, and air brakes, it is actually about George Westinghouse's invention of the air brake. The correct answer is D.
8	B	Even though Vanderbilt felt Westinghouse was a fool, Westinghouse kept trying. The passage specifically states that Westinghouse went on to try another railroad that listened to his ideas and tested his air brake. The correct answer is B.

Question No.	Answer	Detailed Explanations
9	C	While the fact that Westinghouse invented something very important, the air brake, shows that he is smart and he did demonstrate that he is courteous in his interactions with Vanderbilt, he is best described as determined because he did not give up. Only Vanderbilt described Westinghouse as foolish. The correct answer is C.
10	A	While each of the answer choices are true, only answer choice A illustrates how books were important to mountain men and that was because they were hard to get.

Lesson 6: Central Idea Of The Text

Question No.	Answer	Detailed Explanations
1	B	The central idea is that mountain men liked Shakespeare, even if they could not read. Sentence six exemplifies this idea the most.
2	D	More men had Shakespeare than the Bible, and they memorized Shakespeare. That shows how much they loved it.
3	A	The fact that mountain men carried books around for years does not directly prove that they liked Shakespeare best.
4	B	The only answer that is a clear central idea is answer choice B. Option C is a supporting detail. Options A and D are not mentioned.
5	B	Central ideas are general. If a statement is too specific, then it might be a supporting detail and not the central idea.
6	D	The central idea of a passage is supported by details that follow it. That's why the answer is D.
7	A	If you decided on A. Sentences #9 and #10 help the reader remember the definition of homograph and homophone, you made the best choice. The purpose of those details is to help the reader remember the difference between the two terms: homophone and homograph.
8	A	If you looked first at Sentences #1 and #10, you were checking wisely. The central idea of a paragraph is often the first or the last sentence. In this case, Sentence #10 is a supporting detail, and Sentence #1 is the central idea.
9	A	If you looked first at Sentence #3 and then chose A, you made the right decision. Supporting details generally follow the idea they're supporting.
10	B	If you selected B, Sentence #6, you made the right choice. The supporting details often follow immediately the sentence they support.

Lesson 7: Summary Of Text

Question No.	Answer	Detailed Explanations
1	B	Answer choice B is correct because the story specifically says that the policeman asked the writer for his name and address. You assume that the man gave it to him.
2	B	By reading this you can conclude that Thomas likes sports. Based on the fact that Thomas plays so many sports and likes to run in his free time, we can conclude that he likes sports.
3	D	Because he is being so careful, you know that ladders can be dangerous. The correct answer is D. Age is never mentioned, neither is ladders being easy or fun.
4	A	The correct answer is A. The paragraph mentions nothing about students who enjoy math and it doesn't mention how many to buy. It also does not say anything about not needing all of the items.
5	A	The passage is positive about younger siblings, so the answer choice will be positive. It is obvious that the author of the passage thinks that having younger siblings is great.
6	A	The correct answer is A. Because he spent all of the 5 dollars at the candy store, you can assume that he loves candy and did not think spending the money would be useless. That is the only answer that could be right. It never mentions what color his piggy bank is or sharing his candy.
7	B	The correct answer is B. It does not mention whether or not she has had her own room before or not. Her mother is not even mentioned and it said she was decorating her room pink, not purple.
8	B	The correct answer is B. The passage does not mention what state he is moving to, and it also does not mention that he didn't want to stop in other states along the way.
9	C	Answer choice C is correct because the poem has a sad mood. The girl is feeling sad and unhappy. It does not mention that she is afraid and we know that she is not excited. Even though she went to her room, it does not mention that she wanted to be alone.
10	A	Based on the passage, the boy was moving to start a new life. They did not say that he was going on vacation, trying to make it as an actor, or looking for his brother. That's why we can assume that he is starting a new life.

Lesson 8: Evaluating Arguments In Text

Question No.	Answer	Detailed Explanations
1	C	All of the evidence in the passage points to the fact that Jordan was a truly great basketball player. That is why the central idea can be found in answer choice C.
2	D	It was not mentioned in the passage that he was the best player on the team. The only detail that supports the main idea is D, he contributed to many of the Bulls' wins.
3	B	Answer choice B contains two positive things about living in the city. Those are the two sentences that support why the author likes living in the city.
4	C	Answer choice C gives two reasons why young people can't enjoy city life. The other answers do not contain relevant arguments.
5	C	Answer choice C is the only one that mentions gaining weight, and the other answers do not support the argument listed above.
6	C	Answer choice C is the one that most completely goes with the claim that kickboxing is a great form of exercise. Every exercise strengthens the muscles, and it does not mention in the article anything about it being a new trend. It does mention a punching bag, but that is only one part of kickboxing.
7	A	Although all of the answers contain true statements, only answer choice A supports the claim that the cars are innovative in that they are good for the environment.
8	B	The claim, or controlling idea, is usually at the beginning of the paragraph. That is true in this case. The answer is B because that's what the first sentence says.
9	A	The opening sentence is the claim, or the controlling idea i.e., Smartphones are the newest innovative technology out there.
10	B	The claim in this paragraph is the central idea, or controlling idea. It's what the author is trying to convince you of. Answer choice B contains the claim of this passage.

Lesson 9: Characters Responses And Changes

Question No.	Answer	Detailed Explanations
1	D	Answer choice D is correct. There are only three characters in the story; the writer, the writer's friend, and the policeman. Although the actor is mentioned, he is not an actual character.
2	C	The correct answer is C. They were talking about the man in the musical show they had just seen.
3	C	The correct answer is C. The writer is writing in 1st person, and she is the main character in her story.
4	B	The correct answer is B. A major character will be a major part of the story. They will be in more of the story than minor characters.
5	D	The answer is D, all of the above. If you missed this question, go back and re-read the story. Each of these characters contributed action to the story.
6	A	The correct answer is A. The protagonist is often the good guy in a story. He/she is the main character of the story.
7	C	Character traits are the descriptions that authors give their characters. The answer is C.
8	A	Jane was very positive about starting a new school, so we are looking for a positive answer. They are all negative emotions except easy-going.
9	D	The answer choice is D. Risking his own life to save a dog's life shows the man thinks of others more than himself.
10	C	Greg was trying to see how things worked, not being mean to people. The answer choice is C. He was curious.

Lesson 10: Develop Setting

Question No.	Answer	Detailed Explanations
1	A	Based on the details in the passage, it is obvious that the writer is a child still living at home. They discuss doing things that would take place in a home. For those reasons, the correct answer is A.
2	C	The story specifically says that it took place long after people had gone to bed, so answer choice C is correct.
3	D	The correct answer is D. The story specifically says it is morning and she found her mother in the kitchen drinking coffee.
4	D	The correct answer is D. It couldn't be a motel because her mother was in the kitchen sipping coffee. The backyard indicates they are not in an urban area. The most logical answer is that they live in just a regular single family home.
5	B	The answer is B, a forest. The poem never mentions a sports stadium, a house or a palace, but it mentions the forest in the opening line.
6	B	The answer is B. The setting of a story is when and where a story takes place
7	C	The answer is C. The only place mentioned is the outside of Ralphie's house, so that is the only option.
8	C	The correct answer is C. The story specifically says that the robbery was going to take place during dinner time and it was going to be at the green and gold bank
9	B	Because it's her last final exam of high school, you know that the setting of the story is in June.
10	A	The correct answer is A. The month of April is definitely in the spring.

Lesson 11: Analysis Of Key Events And Ideas

Question No.	Answer	Detailed Explanations
1	B	The author used descriptive language to grab the reader's attention. The author wants the reader to be able to imagine what the moment is like. It was raining and the wind was blowing, but the author's point was for the reader to be able to picture it.
2	B	Although the author is talking about the night owl, the point of view is that of the author.
3	A	The poem mentions that it's a night bird and, in the end it is mentioned again. The answer is A.
4	A	Answer A is correct. Upon reading the passage, you will see in the second paragraph that it directly says that they found the bones of a lion.
5	A	If you chose A, you read the passage correctly. The last sentence in the first paragraph gives the correct answer.
6	C	If you chose answer C, you got it right. Good Sense told the other men NOT to create the lion.
7	C	Answer C is the correct answer because it's a direct quote in the story that the friend was afraid the singing would disturb others. The policeman was not behind them yet, or at least had not been noticed. There was no mention of the friend being embarrassed.
8	C	The only answer choice that shows a desire to play outside is C.
9	C	Answer choice C is correct. The fact that it goes by stations tells you that you're on a train.
10	Ring	Ring. This is given in the very first paragraph of the passage.

Lesson 12: Conclusions Drawn From The Text

Question No.	Answer	Detailed Explanations
1	A	The correct answer is A. Sarah's mother told her that it was going to rain, but Sarah chose to ignore her mother's advice. None of the other answers are true. There is no evidence that she doesn't love her mother, and if she didn't like getting wet then she would have definitely listened to her mother. She did not obey her mother, so answer choice D is not correct.
2	C	The correct answer is C. Sarah would not have argued about whether or not to take an umbrella if it were raining. She would not need an umbrella if it were snowing or if it were warm.
3	B	The correct answer is B. We can tell that it is a negative emotion that the boy is feeling - so that eliminates A and D. If he were scared, he would likely want to be WITH people, not away from them.
4	C	The correct answer is C. All of the foods mentioned were breakfast foods, so you can assume that breakfast is being cooked. Also, coffee is usually brewed first thing in the morning.
5	D	In this day and age, it is not likely that the store owner would let him pay him later or work off the candy. John would have to go home and get the money and walk back to the store.
6	D	D is the correct answer. The story specifically says that he did not like books and that he was very clever. Nothing was said in the story that he did not like the other boys.
7	C	The correct answer is C. If the article is saying that these people need to be active, then we can assume that they normally do a lot of sitting.
8	D	The answer is D. The passage specifically says that it was raining and there was no sign of it stopping. The passage does not mention wintry weather or sunny day.
9	C	The answer is C. The fact that the officers called him sir is the only detail that shows that it is a male.
10	C	The correct answer is C. The dog hid under the table AFTER the loud noise, so we can assume that the dog was scared by the loud noises associated with the thunderstorm.

Lesson 13: Structure Of Text

Question No.	Answer	Detailed Explanations
1	B	If you chose B, the missing sentence should be second, you made the best choice. Although it says "Start," you cannot start until you know what you are starting to do, so the missing sentence should not be first. You should select the freshest bread before you take the pieces of it, so the missing sentence should not be third, and it would not make sense in the fourth position.
2	C	If you chose C, the missing sentence should be third, you picked the right answer. The phrase, "continue the aerobic training" lets you know that aerobic training had to have already begun at some point, and it is mentioned in the second sentence.
3	B	If you chose B, the missing sentence should be second, you picked the best response. The definition of potpourri should come before it is mentioned that they were originally made in France, and that the flowers and leaves sat for months.
4	B	If you chose B, you made the right decision. Only option B gives the arrangement that would be a good sequence for the sentences.
5	A	If you picked A, you made the best choice. If the paragraph doesn't begin with sentence 4, the reader will not know what the paragraph is talking about, and sentence 4 is only offered once as the first choice.
6	A	If you put the paragraph in reverse order, it reads perfectly. That is why A is the correct answer.
7	C	This piece gives information, so answer choice C is correct.
8	A	If the paper were written by Westinghouse and about his experience, then it would be a personal narrative.
9	D	All of the above mentioned things are part of an essay. Answer choice D is correct.
10	D	All of these things are part of a business letter.

Lesson 14: Cite Textual Evidence

Question No.	Answer	Detailed Explanations
1	A	The text specifically states that an empty gallery had 42,000 germs but when filled with people, that same gallery had nearly 5,000,000 germs. One can then conclude that a crowded space will hold more germs. The correct answer is A.
2	D	While Louis Pasteur discovered germs there is no evidence in the story to support that he liked counting germs. Yes, germs are too small to be seen with the naked eye but they can be seen using powerful microscopes. Even though people do carry germs, the best concluding statement from this passage would be that there are fewer germs in fresh air. The correct answer is D.
3	D	Throughout the passage, each of the options is pointed out as something significant George Washington did in order to make him a great man. One can draw the conclusion that each factor makes him a great man.
4	C	The text implies that George Washington was not interested in being powerful; therefore Answer B would not be a correct choice. There is no evidence within the text that either supports or disputes that George Washington was a kind man. While his actions certainly showed that he was a smart man, the fact that George Washington was a strong leader is implied in how he led his army as well as knowing when it was his time to share the power by leaving office
5	B	At the beginning of the passage, the text not only states that George Washington is the most popular president but also specifically states that he was elected by a unanimous vote which means that everyone voted for him thus giving him the popular vote.
6	B	In the last paragraph, the passage states that Vanderbilt regretted dismissing Westinghouse's idea of an air brake. As a result, one can conclude that Vanderbilt regretted not taking the time to hear about Westinghouse's invention. The correct answer is B.
7	A	While it is true that Michael Jordan did shave his head, it does not support the idea that he is the greatest basketball player of all time; whereas all the other statements do support this idea. The correct answer is A.

Question No.	Answer	Detailed Explanations
8	B	While Michael Jordan did star in a movie with Bugs Bunny, this is not the most significant part of the passage. Yes, it tells a little about Michael Jordan's life but it is not his life story, it is merely highlights of his career as a famous basketball player. Since the passage tells primarily about Michael Jordan as a basketball player and all he has accomplished, it can be concluded that the author wrote the passage to show what a great basketball player he is. The correct answer is B.
9	D	The passage specifically states that our moon is thought to influence the lives of humans. Therefore, the correct answer is D.
10	A	There is no evidence in the passage which shows that either our moon is less powerful because we only have one or that our moon is bigger than Jupiter's. The text does suggest that people believe the moon causes crazy things to happen like more births, deaths, and people falling in love but there is no proof these things happen. The only thing the passage says for sure, is that people do believe that "looney" things happen and since looney is a synonym for crazy, the correct answer is A.

Lesson 15: Understanding Author's Purpose and Point of View

Question No.	Answer	Detailed Explanations
1	C	The passage is trying to persuade the reader as to why dogs are better pets than cats. The correct answer is C.
2	A	The passage is giving information on how words are added to or deleted from the dictionary. The correct answer is A.
3	B	The passage is explaining how to make a peanut butter and jelly sandwich. The correct answer is B.
4	B	The passage is giving directions with no narrator, therefore it is told from second person point of view.
5	A	The passage is giving information about germs. The correct answer is A.
6	C	While the passage says that football is an exciting sport and that there is never a dull moment, the author does not use persuasive language aimed at convincing the reader. Also, the passage does not tell a story. It does, however, tell about what happens at a game. The correct answer is C.
7	A	The passage ends by saying "you should eat vegetables at least 3 meals a day." It also gives information to backup why this is important. Therefore, the passage is trying to convince readers to eat more vegetables. The correct answer is A.
8	D	Throughout the passage, each of the options is pointed out as something significant George Washington did in order to make him a great man. One can draw the conclusion that each factor makes him a great man.
9	B	While Michael Jordan did star in a movie with Bugs Bunny, this is not the most significant part of the passage. Yes, it tells a little about Michael Jordan's life but it is not his life story, it is merely highlights of his career as a famous basketball player. Since the passage tells primarily about Michael Jordan as a basketball player and all he has accomplished, it can be concluded that the author wrote the passage to show what a great basketball player he is. The correct answer is B.
10	C	Since the passage is providing factual information, it is told from third person point of view.

Question No.	Answer	Detailed Explanations
11	B	Based on what he says, you can tell that these words are from the wolf's perspective. Answer choice B is correct
12	A	In the above passage the wolf claims that allergies were to blame and he didn't want to hurt the pigs. That is very different from the traditional story.
13	B	He is trying to act innocent by saying he never meant to hurt the pigs.
14	C	Because "I" is used, we know that it is written from first person point of view.
15	C	The story does not use I or you; therefore, it is written in third person.
16	A	This passage was definitely from Little Red Riding Hood's perspective. The mother is never mentioned, but the wolf is. Therefore, it can't be from his perspective.
17	C	Answer choice C is correct. She is very sweet and innocent in the original story. She believes things that most of us wouldn't.
18	D	She wanted people to think she could have handled herself just fine against the wolf and that she wasn't scared at all.
19	C	Answer choice C is correct. The author clearly says that owls have the right to hoot if men have the right to speak.
20	D	Anytime someone is giving instructions or telling you what to do, it will be written in second person. D is the correct answer.

Lesson 16: Figurative Words And Phrases

Question No.	Answer	Detailed Explanations
1	A	The answer is A. "dead to the world" means that he was asleep. He would not stay at home if he was not breathing or unconscious; he would be removed immediately and his family would be upset.
2	A	Being in hot water means being in trouble, so answer choice A is correct.
3	A	The correct answer is A. There is no such thing as a circular file, so the only possibility is the trashcan. To say that means to throw something away.
4	B	Working like a dog means working really hard, so answer choice B is correct. This is a common saying.
5	A	Mules are known to be stubborn, so answer choice A is correct.
6	B	A mountain of work is a lot of work. Answer choice B is correct.
7	C	A train wreck causes a big mess on the tracks. Answer choice C is correct.
8	D	Being a star doesn't mean you have to be famous. When you are really good at something, you are said to be "a star". Answer choice D is correct.
9	D	Being a rock means that you are there for someone to lean on. Answer choice D is correct.
10	D	When someone says they feel like a million bucks, it means they feel great. The correct answer is D. Elated means the same thing as happy. Discontented means the opposite.

Chapter 4

Author's Purpose and Craft

Chapter 4

Lesson 1: Comparing Author's Writing To Another

"If your actions inspire others to dream more, learn more, do more and become more, you are a leader." - John Quincy Adams

"The key to successful leadership today is influence, not authority." - Kenneth Blanchard

1. **Pick the right statement that brings out the meaning of the above quotations.**

    Ⓐ Adams talks about actions, whereas Blanchard talks of authority.
    Ⓑ Adams talks about leadership by inspiration, whereas Blanchard talks of leadership by influence.
    Ⓒ Adams talks about inspiration, whereas Blanchard talks of influence.
    Ⓓ Adams talks about leadership, whereas Blanchard talks of success.

Read the following passage and answer the questions that follows.

The square is probably the best known of the quadrilaterals shapes. It is defined as having all sides equal. All its interior angles are right angles (90°). From this, it follows that the opposite sides are also parallel. A square is simply a specific case of a regular polygon, in this case with 4 sides. All the facts and properties described for regular polygons apply to a square.

The rectangle, like the square, is one of the most commonly known quadrilaterals shapes. It is defined as having all four interior angles 90° (right angles). The opposite sides of a rectangle are parallel and congruent.

2. **A similarity between a square and rectangle is that _____.**

    Ⓐ all the sides are equal in both the figures
    Ⓑ only opposite sides are equal in both the figures
    Ⓒ all the interior angles are right angles
    Ⓓ none of the angles are right angles

3. **A difference between a square and rectangle is that _____.**

    Ⓐ all sides are equal in a square, whereas only opposite sides are equal in a rectangle.
    Ⓑ all the interior angles are right angles.
    Ⓒ only opposite sides are equal in both the figures.
    Ⓓ both are quadrilaterals.

Read the statements carefully and answer the questions that follow.

1. Teachers who inspire know that teaching is like cultivating a garden, and those who would have nothing to do with thorns must never attempt to gather flowers.
~Author Unknown

2. Teachers who inspire realize that there will always be rocks in the road ahead of us. They will be stumbling blocks or stepping stones; it all depends on how we use them.
~Author Unknown

4. **While the first author says that teaching is like cultivating a garden, the second author says that _____.**

   Ⓐ those teachers who would have nothing to do with thorns must never attempt to gather flowers
   Ⓑ inspiring teachers realize that there will be rocks in the road ahead
   Ⓒ inspiring teachers realize that there will only be stepping stones in the road
   Ⓓ inspiring teachers realize that there will be only flowers and no thorns

5. **Both the quotations are about _____.**

   Ⓐ stumbling blocks
   Ⓑ rocks and stepping stones
   Ⓒ gardens, flowers and thorns
   Ⓓ teachers who inspire

6. **Hurricanes are similar to blizzards because _____.**

   Ⓐ They both are rain storms.
   Ⓑ They both cause heavy destruction.
   Ⓒ They both are man-made storms.
   Ⓓ They both involve snow.

7. **Love is _____ to a roller coaster because there are many twists and turns in both.**

   Ⓐ different
   Ⓑ unequal
   Ⓒ similar
   Ⓓ All of the above

When you wash dishes you want to make sure you use soap to scrub the dirt off and make sure you rinse them clean after.

8. **Which of the tasks below are similar to washing dishes?**

   Ⓐ Cleaning your house
   Ⓑ Washing the laundry
   Ⓒ Folding your clothes
   Ⓓ Cooking dinner

9. **Words that are used to compare things are _____.**

   Ⓐ Like
   Ⓑ Same as
   Ⓒ Both A and B
   Ⓓ In Contrast

10. **A word that is used to contrast two things is _____.**

    Ⓐ Too
    Ⓑ However
    Ⓒ More
    Ⓓ And

Chapter 4

Lesson 2: Compare/contrast One Author's Presentation With Another

"Peace cannot be achieved through violence, it can only be attained through understanding." - Ralph Waldo Emerson

"Peace cannot be kept by force; it can only be achieved by understanding." - Albert Einstein

1. **What do both of these individuals say about peace?**

    Ⓐ You can only have peace by fighting.
    Ⓑ You can only have peace through understanding.
    Ⓒ You can only have peace when everyone gets along.
    Ⓓ Peace is all around us.

"Music is a world within itself, with a language we all understand." - Stevie Wonder

"Without music, life would be a mistake." - Fredrich Nietzsche

2. **What is similar about these two quotations?**

    Ⓐ Both talk about languages.
    Ⓑ Both talk about life.
    Ⓒ Both talk about music.
    Ⓓ They have nothing similar.

3. **Which one of the answers below is a great way to visually compare and contrast information?**

    Ⓐ Venn Diagram
    Ⓑ Chart
    Ⓒ Graph
    Ⓓ All of the above

4. **To compare and contrast means _____.**

    Ⓐ Explain the details about two things
    Ⓑ Explain how two things are different
    Ⓒ Explain how two things are alike
    Ⓓ Explain how two things are alike and different

5. **Lakes and ponds are similar because _____.**

   Ⓐ They are saltwater
   Ⓑ You can fish in them
   Ⓒ You can jet ski in them
   Ⓓ You can sail in them

6. **Snowfall and rainfall are similar. Which of the following is true with both of these?**

   Ⓐ Wet drops that accumulate on the ground and cause hazardous driving conditions
   Ⓑ Large drops that are white and clear
   Ⓒ Wet drops that turn to ice
   Ⓓ Wet drops that disappear when they touch the ground

Read the quotations and then answer the question that follows.

1. "For every disciplined effort there is a multiple reward." - Jim Rohn

2. "Genius is one percent inspiration and ninety-nine percent perspiration." - Thomas Alva Edison

7. **Both Edison and Rohn are talking about the benefit of _____.**

   Ⓐ genius
   Ⓑ reward
   Ⓒ effort
   Ⓓ inspiration

"Friendship is not something you learn in school. But if you haven't learned the meaning of friendship, you really haven't learned anything." - Muhammad Ali

"If you live to be 100, I hope to live to be 100 minus 1 day, so I never have to live without you." - Winnie the Pooh

8. **What do both of these quotations have in common?**

   Ⓐ They are both about living life.
   Ⓑ They are both about friendship.
   Ⓒ They are both about learning.
   Ⓓ They have nothing in common.

Read the quotations and then answer the question that follows.

"Education is the most powerful weapon which you can use to change the world." Nelson Mandela

"Be the change you wish to see in the world." Gandhi

9. **Both of these quotations talk about changing the world. What two contrasting things do they say makes change in the world?**

Ⓐ Education, yourself
Ⓑ Weapons, yourself
Ⓒ Yourself, man
Ⓓ Education; weapons

10. **The desert is hot and dry whereas the _____ are cold and icy.**

Ⓐ Mountains
Ⓑ Forests
Ⓒ Tropical islands
Ⓓ Polar regions

Answer Key and
Detailed Explanations

Chapter 4: Author's Purpose and Craft

Lesson 1: Comparing Author's Writing To Another

Question No.	Answer	Detailed Explanations
1	B	Answer choice B is correct. They are both talking about what types of leadership are best. They weren't just talking about inspiration and influence, but they were talking about leadership by inspiration and influence.
2	C	Based on the passage, we know that in both figures all of the angles are 90 degree angles (right angles). The correct answer is C.
3	A	Based on the passage, we know that a square is defined as having all sides equal whereas the opposite sides of a rectangle are parallel and congruent.
4	B	Answer choice B is correct. Upon careful reading of the passage, you will see that the author specifically says that there will be rocks in the road ahead. The author does not say the rocks will always be stepping stones; some will be stumbling.
5	D	Both passages use metaphors to describe inspirational teachers, with the rocks and thorns being symbols for obstacles in their way. The correct answer is D.
6	B	The only answer statement that is true is B. A hurricane involves rain and a snowstorm involves snow but both storms can cause heavy destruction.
7	C	Similar is the same as "like." That is why the answer is C.
8	B	Answer choice B is the most similar because you use soap and water and have to rinse and dry them.
9	C	Like and Same as are both words we use to compare things. Contrast is a word we use to tell how things are different. The answer is C.
10	B	"However" is the only word that is a word you could use to contrast something. It is similar to the word "but."

Lesson 2: Compare/contrast One Author's Presentation With Another

Question No.	Answer	Detailed Explanations
1	B	Both men are talking about how peace can only be attained through non-violence and understanding. The correct answer is B.
2	C	Both quotations, while having a different message, speak about the importance and value of music. The correct answer choice is C.
3	D	You can use all of the above to effectively compare and contrast.
4	D	Comparing is seeing how things are alike and contrasting is seeing how they are different. For that reason, the answer is D.
5	B	Ponds are not big enough to jet ski or sail in, and ponds and lakes are fresh water bodies of water. The only answer that is true is B.
6	A	Answer choice A is the only one that describes both rain and snow. The other answers only describe one, either rain or snow.
7	C	Both quotes are about effort, so the correct answer is C.
8	B	Both of these quotes are about friendship even if it is not specifically stated. The correct answer is B.
9	A	While both quotes talk about changing the world, the first quote stresses that education leads to change whereas the second quote suggests that you yourself create change. The correct answer is A.
10	D	Polar regions are the only logical answer because they are cold and icy. The correct answer is D.

Chapter 5

Composition

Chapter 5

Lesson 1: Style Appropriate Task, Purpose, And Audience

Refer the below poster and answer the following questions.

> Tulips Band Concert
> Tuesday, February 26th 8:00 P.M.
> School's Amphitheater All are
> welcome to watch and cheer!

1. **What category does the above poster belong to?**

   Ⓐ Informative poster
   Ⓑ Propaganda poster
   Ⓒ Affirmation poster
   Ⓓ None of the above

2. **According to the above poster which is the venue of the concert?**

   Ⓐ Band Concert Hall
   Ⓑ Amphitheater
   Ⓒ School Gym
   Ⓓ None of the above

3. **What do you understand by reading the above poster?**

   Ⓐ There is a band concert
   Ⓑ That the band concert is in February
   Ⓒ The band concert is in the Amphitheater
   Ⓓ All of the above

4. **Who is the target audience for this poster?**

   Ⓐ students
   Ⓑ teachers
   Ⓒ parents
   Ⓓ all of the above

5. Determine the author's main purpose in the following passage from an analysis of Huckleberry Finn by Keith Neilson, in which he discusses Huckleberry Finn's dilemma over turning in a runaway slave that he believes to be the legal property of his owners:

Given opportunities to turn Jim in, Huck finds that he cannot; his feelings toward Jim have become too strong. Huck begins to experience emotions that he has never had before – personal concern, loyalty, guilt, and fear. He is soon forced to accept Jim, not as a slave, but as a human being, and once he does that, all the contradictions of his moral situation become evident to the reader, if not immediately to Huck. He is forced to consciously choose between loyalty to his society's morality and his friend's freedom. That moment of choice is one of the great moments in American literature.

Ⓐ narrative
Ⓑ expository/informational
Ⓒ persuasive
Ⓓ entertainment

6. Determine the author's main purpose in the following passage from Huckleberry Finn, by Mark Twain, in which Huckleberry Finn confronts his dilemma over turning in the runaway slave, Jim:

I got to thinking over our trip down the river, but somehow I couldn't seem to strike no places to harden me against him, but only the other kind. At last I struck the time I saved him by telling the men we had smallpox aboard, and he was so grateful and said I was the best friend old Jim ever had in the world...I was a-trembling because I'd got to decide forever betwixt two things, and I knowed it. I studied a minute, sort of holding my breath, then says to myself, "All right, then. I'll never turn him in. I'll go to hell."

Ⓐ narrative
Ⓑ expository/informational
Ⓒ persuasive
Ⓓ biography

7. Choose an appropriate title for the below passage.

The sky was dark and overcast. It had been raining all night long and there was no sign of it stopping. I thought that my Sunday would be ruined.

As it poured outside, I settled down by the window to watch the rain. The park opposite my house looked even more green and fresh than usual. The branches of the tall trees swayed so hard in the strong wind that I thought they would break. A few children were splashing about in the mud puddles and having a wonderful time. I wished that I could join them too! There were very few people out on the road and those who were hurried on their way, wrapped in raincoats and carrying umbrellas.

My mother announced that lunch was ready. It was piping hot and very welcoming in the damp weather.
We spent the afternoon listening to music and to the downpour outside.

In the evening we chatted and made paper boats that we meant to sail in the stream of water outside. It was not a bad day after all!

Ⓐ The Green Park
Ⓑ A Bad Day
Ⓒ A Rainy Day
Ⓓ The Water That Fell From the sky

8. What is the main purpose of the below poem?

Faster than fairies, faster than witches,
Bridges and houses, hedges and ditches,
And charging along like troops in a battle,
All through the meadows the horses and cattle,
All of the sights of the hill and the plain,
Fly as thick as driving rain,
And ever again, in the wink of an eye,
Painted stations whistle by.

Here is a child who clambers and scrambles,
All by himself and gathering brambles;
Here is a tramp who stands and gazes,
And there is the green for stringing the daisies;
Here is a cart run away in the road,
Lumping along with man and load;
And here is a mill and there is a river,
Each a glimpse and gone forever.

-- R. L. STEVENSON

Ⓐ The Green Park
Ⓑ A Bad Day
Ⓒ A Rainy Day
Ⓓ The Water That Fell From the sky

9. **If you hear this in the middle of a school day by the principal...**

Who is the intended audience?

"Stop! You may not run in the hallway!"

Ⓐ A teacher
Ⓑ A principal
Ⓒ A parent
Ⓓ A student

10. **Who is the intended audience?**

"I promise to help get better food in the cafeteria and to make sure we have more days off from school. So, please vote for me!"

Ⓐ The voters in the world.
Ⓑ The voters in a company.
Ⓒ The voters in a town.
Ⓓ The voters in a school.

Chapter 5

Lesson 2: Develop And Strengthen Planning

Everywhere around us there are millions of tiny living things called germs. They are so tiny that they can be seen only under the most powerful microscope. Some of these germs are no wider than twenty-five thousandth of an inch!

Louis Pasteur, the great French scientist, was the first to prove that germs exist. The germs in the air can be counted. The number of germs around us, especially in crowded rooms is tremendous. Certain scientists counted 42,000 germs in approximately one cubic meter of air in a picture gallery when it was empty. But when the gallery was crowded with people, they found nearly 5,000,000 germs in the same place. In the open air germs are less abundant. There are fewer germs in country air than in town air. We see at once how important it is, therefore, to live as much as possible in the open air, and for the rooms we live in to always be well ventilated by fresh air.

1. **If you were asked to write an essay on the great French scientist Louis Pasteur, which of the following would you pick for your research?**

   Ⓐ A journal about germs
   Ⓑ A science magazine
   Ⓒ A biography of Louis Pasteur
   Ⓓ A science museum

The forest's sentinel
Glides silently across the hill
And perches in an old pine tree,
A friendly presence his!
No harm can come
From night bird on the prowl.
His cry is mellow,
Much softer than a peacock's call.
Why then this fear of owls
Calling in the night?
If men must speak,
Then owls must hoot-
They have the right.
On me it casts no spell:
Rather, it seems to cry,
"The night is good- all's well, all's well."

-- RUSKIN BOND

2. **If you had to write a poem about owls, which of the following would help you in your research?**

    Ⓐ Encyclopedia of birds
    Ⓑ Your imagination about owls
    Ⓒ An article about owls
    Ⓓ All of the above

3. **Which of the following statements is true?**

    Ⓐ The first step in writing is picking a topic for your writing task
    Ⓑ The second step is to publish the writing
    Ⓒ The last step is to edit the writing
    Ⓓ The third step is to do the pre-writing work

4. **A _____ helps to get the ideas of the writer on paper.**

    Ⓐ proofreader
    Ⓑ rough draft
    Ⓒ revision
    Ⓓ setting

5. **All types of writing start with _____.**

   (A) proofreading
   (B) editing
   (C) revising
   (D) ideas

6. **Where do original ideas to write about come from?**

   (A) Ideas to write about may come from one's own experience or someone else's.
   (B) Ideas to write about may come from copying someone else's.
   (C) Ideas to write about may come by not thinking about it.
   (D) All of the above

7. **All narrative stories require _____?**

   (A) a main character
   (B) good descriptive writing
   (C) interesting problems
   (D) all of the above

8. **A well written, interesting piece of narrative writing has _____.**

   (A) a rough draft
   (B) a beginning, middle and an end
   (C) descriptive details
   (D) Both 'B' and 'C'

9. **A _____ is the person, animal or thing that the story is about.**

   (A) supporting character
   (B) main character
   (C) villain
   (D) mentor

10. **In a narrative, _____ happen to the main character as he/she/it tries to solve the problem.**

    (A) no events
    (B) only good events
    (C) only bad events
    (D) a sequence of events

Chapter 5

Lesson 3: Transitions To Clarify

1. **Which of the sentences best combines these two sentences?**

   I needed to go to the store. I didn't have any money.

   Ⓐ I didn't have any money because I needed to go to the store.
   Ⓑ I didn't have any money; furthermore, I needed to go to the store.
   Ⓒ I didn't have any money although I needed to go to the store.
   Ⓓ i didn't have any money; therefore, I needed to go to the store.

2. **The story ended well; _____, it ended with the words "happily ever after".**

   Ⓐ although
   Ⓑ in fact
   Ⓒ however
   Ⓓ because

3. **What part of a sentence or combined sentences is the transition word located?**

   Ⓐ middle of the sentence or sentences
   Ⓑ beginning of the sentence or sentences
   Ⓒ both A and B
   Ⓓ neither A or B

4. **Most people have a cell phone these days. Some people can not afford them.**

   Ⓐ Some people can't afford cell phones although most people have one these days.
   Ⓑ Most people have a cell phone these days, and some people can't afford them.
   Ⓒ Most people have a cell phone these days; therefore, some people can't afford them.
   Ⓓ Most people have a cell phone these days; in fact, some people can't afford them.

5. **In the following paragraph, there are blanks for transition words. Choose the best transition word from the answer choices.**

Once upon a time there was a little girl named Lacy. (1) _____ she was a very sweet little girl, she always got into trouble. Her mother would give her warning after warning every day. (2)_____, Lacy just didn't listen.

One day she disobeyed her mother ten times. Her mother had to discipline her (3) _____ it made them both cry. (4) _____, Lacy learned to obey her mother.

What is the best transition word for blank #1?

Ⓐ However
Ⓑ in fact
Ⓒ Although
Ⓓ Consequently

6. **In the following paragraph, there are blanks for transition words. Choose the best transition word from the answer choices.**

Once upon a time there was a little girl named Lacy. (1)_____ she was a very sweet little girl, she always got into trouble. Her mother would give her warning after warning every day. (2)_____, Lacy just didn't listen.

(3)_____, one day she disobeyed ten times in one day. He mother had to spank her (4) _____ it made them both cry. (5) _____, Lacy learned to obey her mother.

What is the best transition word for blank #2?

Ⓐ However
Ⓑ In addition
Ⓒ Although
Ⓓ In conclusion

7. **In the following paragraph, there are blanks for transition words. Choose the best transition word from the answer choices.**

Once upon a time there was a little girl named Lacy. (1)_____ she was a very sweet little girl, she always got into trouble. Her mother would give her warning after warning every day. (2)_____, Lacy just didn't listen.

(3)_____, one day she disobeyed ten times in one day. He mother had to spank her (4) _____ it made them both cry. (5) _____, Lacy learned to obey her mother.

What is the best transition word for blank #3?

Ⓐ Eventually
Ⓑ Therefore
Ⓒ In fact
Ⓓ However

8. **In the following paragraph, there are blanks for transition words. Choose the best transition word from the answer choices.**

Once upon a time there was a little girl named Lacy. (1)_____ she was a very sweet little girl, she always got into trouble. Her mother would give her warning after warning every day. (2)_____, Lacy just didn't listen.

(3)_____, one day she disobeyed ten times in one day. He mother had to spank her (4) _____ it made them both cry. (5) _____, Lacy learned to obey her mother.

What is the best transition word for blank #4?

Ⓐ therefore
Ⓑ although
Ⓒ in addition
Ⓓ it even

9. **In the following paragraph, there are blanks for transition words. Choose the best transition word from the answer choices.**

Once upon a time there was a little girl named Lacy. (1)_____ she was a very sweet little girl, she always got into trouble. Her mother would give her warning after warning every day. (2)_____, Lacy just didn't listen.

(3)_____, one day she disobeyed ten times in one day. He mother had to spank her (4) _____ it made them both cry. (5) _____, Lacy learned to obey her mother.

What is the best transition word for blank #5?

Ⓐ Eventually
Ⓑ Finally
Ⓒ Both A and B would work
Ⓓ None of the above

10. **Which of the transitions below are a good way to end a paragraph?**

Ⓐ Furthermore
Ⓑ In conclusion
Ⓒ However
Ⓓ Equally important

Chapter 5

Lesson 4: Vary Sentence Style

1. **From the choices provided, select the best way to combine the given sentences.**

   Thomas Alva Edison invented the electric bulb. He did this in 1879.

   Ⓐ Thomas Alva Edison invented it in 1879. It was the electric bulb.
   Ⓑ Thomas Alva Edison invented the electric bulb in 1879.
   Ⓒ Thomas Alva Edison invented the electric bulb since1879.
   Ⓓ Thomas Alva Edison invented, in 1879, the electric bulb.

2. **From the choices provided, select the best way to combine the given sentences.**

   Polar bears are fierce creatures. Grizzly bears are the same.

   Ⓐ Neither polar bears nor grizzly bears are fierce creatures.
   Ⓑ Polar bears and grizzly bears are fierce creatures.
   Ⓒ Polar bears are fierce creatures but grizzly bears are the same.
   Ⓓ Polar bears or grizzly bears are the same fierce creatures.

3. **From the choices provided, select the best way to combine the given sentences.**

   I am hungry. I have not eaten since last night.

   Ⓐ I am hungry because I have not eaten anything since last night.
   Ⓑ I am hungry, but I have not eaten anything since last night.
   Ⓒ I am hungry, and I have not eaten anything since last night.
   Ⓓ Before I have not eaten anything since last night, I am hungry.

4. **From the choices provided, select the best way to combine the given sentences.**

   The witness refused to say anything. He was put in jail.

   Ⓐ The witness refused to say anything; therefore, he was put in jail.
   Ⓑ Although the witness refused to say anything, he was put in jail.
   Ⓒ Before the witness refused to say anything, he was put in jail.
   Ⓓ The witness refused to say anything, after all he was put in jail.

5. From the choices provided, select the best way to combine the given sentences.

I will not say anything. I will be misquoted.

Ⓐ I will not say anything and I will be misquoted.
Ⓑ I will not say anything before I will be misquoted.
Ⓒ I will not say anything because I will be misquoted.
Ⓓ I will not say anything so I will be misquoted.

6. From the choices provided, select the best way to combine the given sentences.

We had made plans to go for a picnic. The rain ruined our plans.

Ⓐ We had made plans to go for a picnic; however, the rain ruined our plans.
Ⓑ We had made plans to go for a picnic and the rain ruined our plans.
Ⓒ We had made plans to go for a picnic; although, the rain ruined our plans.
Ⓓ The rain ruined our plans. Therefore, we had to go for the picnic.

7. From the choices provided, select the best way to combine the given sentences.

The cactus is drying up. The cactus is not getting enough sunlight.

Ⓐ The cactus is drying up, and the cactus is not getting enough sunlight.
Ⓑ The cactus is drying up; although the cactus is not getting enough sunlight.
Ⓒ The cactus is drying up because it is not getting enough sunlight.
Ⓓ The cactus is drying up; therefore, it is not getting enough sunlight.

8. From the choices provided, select the best way to combine the given sentences.

My sister ate a big meal. She could not play after that.

Ⓐ My sister ate a big meal and she could not play after that.
Ⓑ Because my sister ate a big meal, she could not play after that.
Ⓒ Although my sister ate a big meal, she could play after that.
Ⓓ My sister ate a big meal, and so she could not play after that.

9. From the choices provided, select the best way to combine the given sentences.

Rainy days can be boring. Rainy days can be fun too.

Ⓐ Rainy days can be boring, rainy days can be fun too.
Ⓑ Rainy days can be boring; therefore, rainy days can be fun too.
Ⓒ Rainy days can be boring. So rainy days can be fun too.
Ⓓ Rainy days can be boring, but rainy days can be fun too.

10. From the choices provided, select the best way to combine the given sentences.

The reviews for the movie are great. I would love to see it.

Ⓐ The reviews for the movie are great, but I would love to see it.
Ⓑ The reviews for the movie are great; however, I would love to see it.
Ⓒ The reviews for the movie are great and I would love to see it.
Ⓓ Because the reviews for the movie are great, I would love to see it.

Chapter 5

Lesson 5: Introduce And Conclude The Topic

As long ago as 300 B.C., a Greek astronomer named Aristarchus came to the conclusion that the sun stood still while the earth and other planets revolved around it. Using only his naked eye because there were no telescopes in those days, Aristarchus determined that the passing of night and day and the changing of the seasons could all be explained by viewing the heavens in that way.

1. **Select the best introductory sentence for the paragraph.**

    Ⓐ A few astronomers in ancient times understood the organization of the universe long before most people knew about it.
    Ⓑ It was many centuries before the workings of the universe were understood by scientists.
    Ⓒ Many ancient astronomers were confused about the revolution of the earth around the sun.
    Ⓓ A telescope is not always necessary for astronomical observations.

The Greek-Egyptian astronomer Ptolemy claimed that the earth stood still in space, with the sun, moon, and stars revolving around it. The bodies all moved at the same speed in perfect circular orbits. He believed that the universe was made up of a series of globes, one inside each other. Each globe was formed of a different kind of element. The earth was the innermost, surrounded by globes of air, fire, and gas.

2. **Select the best introductory sentence for the following paragraph.**

    Ⓐ Ptolemy was believed for many centuries, although he was completely wrong.
    Ⓑ Many scientists made wrong guesses about the earth itself.
    Ⓒ Ptolemy's theory about the nature of the universe was elegant and easy to understand.
    Ⓓ People were comforted by believing the earth was the center of the universe.

Frogs are amphibians that belong to a group called vertebrates. Frogs have very strong legs for leaping great distances. Frogs can be found anywhere in the world. Frogs are slimy, so often people are reluctant to pick them up. Frogs eat bugs and worms.

3. **Please choose the best concluding statement.**

    Ⓐ Frogs are green.
    Ⓑ As you can see, frogs are interesting creatures to learn about.
    Ⓒ Frogs don't like to be touched by humans.
    Ⓓ Frogs have good eyesight to help them catch food and avoid enemies.

Reading helps you increase your vocabulary and therefore be able to write and speak better. Reading helps develop your mind and increase your knowledge intake. Reading helps you discover new things and aids in developing your imagination. If you do not know how to read well, you will not be able to find a good job, as this is a vital skill in the workplace. Reading is one of the key skills you need to learn early in your life.

4.   Please choose the best introductory sentence.

Ⓐ Reading is an important skill that you must learn.
Ⓑ You are an idiot if you don't learn to read.
Ⓒ Reading helps you.
Ⓓ Reading and writing are important skills to know.

In the first stage, the old items are collected and sorted. They are cleaned, so they will be ready to be recreated into new products. The second stage involves manufacturing new products from the old items. The last stage is when the newly recycled goods are purchased by consumers. The more people who buy recycled products, the more successful recycling will be.

5.   Please choose the introductory sentence that best fits.

Ⓐ There are many things to do when you recycle.
Ⓑ It is very important to recycle.
Ⓒ Recycling is good for the environment.
Ⓓ There are three different stages in the recycling process.

Running is a great sport and form of exercise. Most people need to run 3-4 times a week to improve their skills and run faster. Runners also like to do sprint workouts, which help increase a runner's speed. When you run, it is important to stay hydrated before, during, and after your run. You also need to stretch before and after you run to make sure you keep your muscles loose, so you do not get injured.

6.   Please choose the best concluding statement.

Ⓐ Running increases your metabolism.
Ⓑ Changing the distance you run each day is important to keep your body from staying in a routine.
Ⓒ Running can cause many injures.
Ⓓ As long as you do it right, running is one of the best ways to stay in shape.

7. Use your own words to make up an introductory sentence for the following passage.

The leaves are changing color. The air feels crisp and fresh. School is starting, and people are buying new clothes and supplies. There is a feeling of fresh starts and new beginnings.

8. Use your own words to make up an introductory sentence for the following passage.

We were behind for the entire first quarter, and in the second quarter, things just got worse. We were playing badly, intimidated by their skill and confidence. Every time they made a basket, we got more and more sad and depressed. It was starting to look like we had no chance at the championship, when suddenly it all started to turn around.

9. Use your own words to make up an introductory sentence for the following passage.

He can keep a secret, for one thing. Not every best friend can do that. Another good reason is that he helps me with everything I need to do. He makes me laugh, and we always have fun together. I hope we'll be friends all our lives.

10. Use your own words to make up an introductory sentence for the following passage.

He always made me do my homework before I could go out to play. I had to do chores on Saturday before I had free time. If I broke something, I had to fix it. If I made a mess, I had to clean it up. If I hurt someone's feelings, I had to apologize. Now I'm glad about all of those habits. Maybe he wasn't so mean after all!

Chapter 5

Lesson 6: Introduce Headings And Graphics

1. **You are asked to do a project on wild animals in Africa. Which appropriate heading would you choose for such information?**

   Ⓐ Wild Animals
   Ⓑ Animals
   Ⓒ Africa
   Ⓓ Africa's Wild Animals

2. **Use the table of contents to answer the question given below:**

How To Be Healthy

Table of Contents	Page#
1. What is health	8-10
2. The human body	11-18
3. What you need to eat to maintain good health	19-26
4. Mental health	27-32
5. How to guard against diseases	33-40
6. Exercise and health	41-50

If you want to not get sick, which pages of the above book would you go to?

Ⓐ pages 27-32
Ⓑ pages 33-40
Ⓒ pages 8-10
Ⓓ pages 41-50

3. The table of contents in a book will help you find names of chapters in the book and the page numbers where they occur. The chapters have a name and are usually numbered.

Use the table of contents to answer the question given below:

How To Be Healthy

Table of Contents	Page#
1. What is health	8-10
2. The human body	11-18
3. What you need to eat to maintain good health	19-26
4. Mental health	27-32
5. How to guard against diseases	33-40
6. Exercise and health	41-50

How many chapters are there in this book?

Ⓐ 6
Ⓑ 7
Ⓒ 1
Ⓓ 50

4. The table of contents in a book will help you find names of chapters in the book and the page numbers where they occur. The chapters have a name and are usually numbered.

Use the table of contents to answer the question given below:

How To Be Healthy

Table of Contents	Page#
1. What is health	8-10
2. The human body	11-18
3. What you need to eat to maintain good health	19-26
4. Mental health	27-32
5. How to guard against diseases	33-40
6. Exercise and health	41-50

If you want to find out the food that is good for you, which chapter would you go to?

Ⓐ chapter 3
Ⓑ chapter 2
Ⓒ chapter 5
Ⓓ chapter 6

5. Read the following paragraph:

How does the body know to breathe and move?

The central nervous system tells the body what to do.

The nervous system is the control system and the network of communication for the body. The nervous system is made up of nerves, the spinal cord and the brain.

The nerves control everything we do. They carry messages that tell us to move, to breathe, to feel and to think. Nerves run to the muscles, organs, heart, lungs, blood vessels, brain--even to our teeth and skin.

There are two sets of nerves: the central nervous system and the peripheral (outside) nervous system.

What kind of graphic helps to better understand the above passage?

Ⓐ a scientific drawing of the human nervous system
Ⓑ a scientific drawing of the heart and lungs
Ⓒ a picture of a doctor examining a patient
Ⓓ pictures of books, computer and a seminar

6. Read the following paragraph:

How does the body know to breathe and move?

The central nervous system tells the body what to do.

The nervous system is the control system and the network of communication for the body. The nervous system is made up of nerves, the spinal cord and the brain.

The nerves control everything we do. They carry messages that tell us to move, to breathe, to feel and to think. Nerves run to the muscles, organs, heart, lungs, blood vessels, brain--even to our teeth and skin.

There are two sets of nerves: the central nervous system and the peripheral (outside) nervous system.

Suggest an appropriate heading for the above passage from the choices given below:

Ⓐ How does the body breathe and move?
Ⓑ What does the nervous system do?
Ⓒ The nervous system
Ⓓ Choice 'B' or 'C'

Go through the following headings & subheadings and answer the following questions (for questions 7 - 10).

TRANSPORT SYSTEM IN INDIA
1 Traditional means
   1.1 Walking
   1.2 Palanquin
   1.3 Bullock carts and horse carriages
   1.4 Bicycles
   1.5 Hand-pulled rickshaw
   1.6 Cycle rickshaw
   1.7 Trams
2 Local transport
   2.1 Public transport
   2.1.1 Buses
   2.1.2 Taxi
   2.1.3 Auto Rickshaws
   2.1.4 Suburban Railway
   2.1.5 Metro Rail (Mass Rapid Transit System)
   2.2 Two-wheelers
   2.3 Automobiles
   2.4 Utility vehicles
3 Long distance transport
   3.1 Railway
   3.1.1 International
   3.2 Road
   3.3 Aviation
   3.3.1 Airports
   3.3.2 Heliports
4 Ports and shipping
5 Waterways
6 Bridges
7 Pipelines

7. **How many headings come under the topic: "TRANSPORT SYSTEM IN INDIA"**

   Ⓐ 29
   Ⓑ 7
   Ⓒ 8
   Ⓓ 10

8. **Select the choice that contains any three headings:**

   Ⓐ Railway, International, Road
   Ⓑ Public transport, Buses, Taxi, Auto Rickshaws
   Ⓒ Aviation, Airports, Heliports
   Ⓓ Traditional means, Local transport, Long distance transport

9. **Select the choice that contains any three headings:**

Ⓐ 2.1 Public transport
   2.1.1 Buses
   2.1.2 Taxi
   2.1.3 Auto Rickshaws
   2.1.4 Suburban Railway
   2.1.5 Metro Rail

Ⓑ 2.1 Public transport
   2.1.1 Buses
   2.1.2 Taxi
   2.1.3 Auto Rickshaws
   2.1.4 Suburban Railway
   2.1.5 Metro Rail (Mass Rapid Transit System)
   2.2 Two-wheelers
   2.3 Automobiles
   2.4 Utility vehicles

Ⓒ 2.1 Public transport
   2.2 Two-wheelers
   2.3 Automobiles
   2.4 Utility vehicles

Ⓓ 2.1 Public transport
   2.1.1 Buses
   2.1.2 Taxi
   2.1.3 Auto Rickshaws
   2.1.4 Suburban Railway
   2.1.5 Metro Rail (Mass Rapid Transit System)
   2.2 Two-wheelers
   2.3 Automobiles
   2.4 Utility vehicles
   3 Long distance transport
   3.1 Railway
   3.1.1 International
   3.2 Road
   3.3 Aviation
   3.3.1 Airports
   3.3.2 Heliports
   4 Ports and shipping
   5 Waterways
   6 Bridges
   7 Pipelines

10. After going through the information about 'Transport System in India', you come to understand that Bullock carts and horse carriages are _____.

Ⓐ Long distance transport
Ⓑ the only means of transport in India
Ⓒ means of water transport
Ⓓ Traditional means of transport.

Chapter 5

Lesson 7: Convey Ideas And Descriptive Details

1. **Identify the type, or genre, of the following passage:**

Even without his gun, he was determined to single-handedly even his score with the thugs and pursue justice.

This writing is _____.

Ⓐ humor
Ⓑ an action story
Ⓒ a tall tale
Ⓓ a fairy tale

2. **Identify the type, or genre, of the following passage:**

During the Renaissance, scientists began correcting their mistaken notions about all kinds of things, discarding superstitions and errors that had been handed down to them. New discoveries were the order of the day.

This writing is _____.

Ⓐ biography
Ⓑ fiction
Ⓒ an essay
Ⓓ an autobiography

3. **Identify the type, or genre, of the following passage:**

The castle looked deserted in the foggy night air. There were no lights anywhere, and a strange noise like a muffled human scream was coming from an upper window. The door creaked slowly open when she pushed on it. She hesitated.

This writing is _____.

Ⓐ horror
Ⓑ humor
Ⓒ a fable
Ⓓ a fairy tale

4. Identify the type, or genre, of the following passage:

My dad is serious about our family being fairly quiet during dinner. No phone calls. No visitors. No bickering. Just peace and quiet and pleasant conversation. If we are sent away from the table, there will be no dinner for us later. When he says he wants a quiet meal, he means it.

This writing is _____.

Ⓐ fairy tale
Ⓑ science fiction
Ⓒ realistic fiction
Ⓓ mythology

5. Identify the type, or genre, of the following passage:

Many had died in the labyrinth, unable to find the way out. Those men lacked the advantage Theseus had... he knew how to find his way back the way he had come. Thanks to the help of the princess Ariadne, Theseus had a plan. Fearlessly, he entered the forbidding labyrinth.

This writing is _____.

Ⓐ mythology
Ⓑ humor
Ⓒ horror
Ⓓ persuasive

6. Identify the type, or genre, of the following passage:

The infrared goggles enable you to see in the dark, and your jetpack is equipped with a navigator. Through the jungle, you can see the megasaurs with their laser eyes. You know that you must avoid their gaze if you plan to stay alive.

This writing is _____.

Ⓐ mystery
Ⓑ humor
Ⓒ realistic fiction
Ⓓ science fiction

7. Identify the type, or genre, of the following passage:

Once upon a time, in a kingdom far away from here, there lived the most beautiful princess anyone had ever seen. Her eyes shown like diamonds, her hair was like silk, and her skin was as white as snow.

This writing is _____.

Ⓐ science fiction
Ⓑ horror
Ⓒ a fairy tale
Ⓓ realistic fiction

8. Identify the type, or genre, of the following passage:

The fox stood looking at the grapes dangling above his head. He was hungry and the grapes looked delicious. But he couldn't climb up, jump up, or find anything to make a ladder. "Oh, well," he said as he walked away. "Those grapes are probably sour anyway."

This writing is _____.

Ⓐ realistic fiction
Ⓑ science fiction
Ⓒ a fable
Ⓓ humor

9. Identify the type, or genre, of the following passage:

She was determined to figure it out. How could the thief have broken in? There was no sign that the locks had been tampered with, and no windows were broken. The room showed no evidence of struggle.

This writing is _____.

Ⓐ a fable
Ⓑ a fairy tale
Ⓒ humor
Ⓓ a mystery

10. Identify the type, or genre, of the following passage:

He was the roughest, toughest baby anyone had ever seen. He drank whiskey with his milk, tied up the family dog, and crawled away from home before he was old enough to walk or talk. By the time he was walking around, everyone in Texas knew his name – and they stayed out of his way.

This writing is _____.

Ⓐ science fiction
Ⓑ tall tale
Ⓒ realistic fiction
Ⓓ biography

Chapter 5

Lesson 8: Sensory Language Conveyed

1. **Complete the paragraph with three sentences using sensory language, based on the clue in the introductory sentence.**

   Walking into my grandmother's kitchen, my senses are overwhelmed.

   --.

   --.

   --.

2. **Complete the paragraph with three sentences using sensory language based on the clue in the introductory sentence.**

   There are many things to see at the football game.

   --.

   --.

   --.

3. **Complete the paragraph with three sentences using sensory language based on the clue in the introductory sentence.**

   The night forest is full of sounds.

   --.

   --.

   --.

4. Complete the paragraph with three sentences using sensory language based on the clue in the introductory sentence.

I had many feelings as I fastened my seat belt for my very first airplane trip.

5. Complete the paragraph with three sentences using sensory language based on the clue in the introductory sentence.

I had to plug my ears at the rock concert.

6. Complete the paragraph with three sentences using sensory language based on the clue in the introductory sentence.

My afternoon at the zoo was amazing.

7. **Complete the paragraph with three sentences using sensory language based on the clue in the introductory sentence.**

The snow kept falling fast, and I couldn't believe my eyes.

---.

---.

---.

8. **Complete the paragraph with three sentences using sensory language based on the clue in the introductory sentence.**

I was sure I could learn to ride a horse by just climbing on and taking the reins.

---.

---.

---.

9. **Complete the paragraph with three sentences using sensory language based on the clue in the introductory sentence.**

The fireman pulled up to a burning building.

---.

---.

---.

10. Complete the paragraph with three sentences using sensory language based on the clue in the introductory sentence.

The woman walked into the old house.

---.

---.

---.

Chapter 5

Lesson 9: Develop And Strengthen Revising

1. **Revising a written work helps to _____.**

   Ⓐ correct mistakes, if any
   Ⓑ waste time
   Ⓒ appreciate the written work
   Ⓓ none of the above

2. **Select the remedy that would best repair the following sentence:**

   The airport is about to shut down because of the blizzard and if the plane does not land soon it will have to go on to Dallas.

   Ⓐ The airport is about to shut down because of the blizzard. If the plane does not land soon, it will have to go on to Dallas.
   Ⓑ The airport is about to shut down because of the blizzard and, if the plane does not land soon it will have to go on to Dallas.
   Ⓒ The airport is about to shut down because of the blizzard and if the plane, does not land soon, it will have to go on to Dallas.
   Ⓓ The sentence is correct.

3. **Select the remedy that would best repair the following sentence:**

   The show begins at 1830 hrs make sure you are there before 1815hrs.

   Ⓐ The show begins at 1830 hrs, make sure, you are there before 1815hrs.
   Ⓑ The show begins at 1830 hrs. Make sure you are there before 1815 hrs.
   Ⓒ The show, begins at 1830 hrs, make sure you are there before 1815hrs.
   Ⓓ The show begins at 1830 hrs; make sure, you are there before 1815hrs.

4. **Select the remedy that would best repair the following sentence:**

   The hero planned his moves well in advance and charged at the villain and his associates with gun.

   Ⓐ The hero planned his moves well in advance, and charged at the villain and his associates with gun.
   Ⓑ The hero planned his moves well in advance, and charged at the villian, and his associates with gun.
   Ⓒ The hero planned his moves well in advance and charged at the villian and his associates with a gun.
   Ⓓ The hero planned his moves, well in advance, and charged at the villian and his associates with gun.

5. **Select the remedy that would best repair the following sentence:**

Friends romans and countrymen lend me your ears.

Ⓐ Friends, romans, and countrymen lend me your ears.
Ⓑ Friends romans, and countrymen lend me your ears.
Ⓒ Friends, Romans, and countrymen, lend me your ears.
Ⓓ Friends romans and countrymen, lend me your ears.

6. **Select the remedy that would best repair the following sentence:**

I live in dallas Texas and my son lives in San diego.

Ⓐ I live in Dallas Texas and my son lives in San Diego.
Ⓑ I live in Dallas Texas, and my son lives in San Diego.
Ⓒ I live in dallas, Texas, and my son lives in San diego.
Ⓓ I live in Dallas, Texas, and my son lives in San Diego.

7. **Select the remedy that would best repair the following sentence:**

She was still upset although she had won the oscar.

Ⓐ She was still upset although, she had won the oscar.
Ⓑ She was still upset, although she had won the oscar.
Ⓒ She was still upset although she had won Oscar.
Ⓓ She was still upset although she had won the Oscar.

8. **Combine these short sentences to make a single sentence.**

The city council conducted a study on public transportation The study was lengthy. The study was detailed.

Ⓐ The city council conducted a study on public transportation and the study was lengthy and the study was detailed.
Ⓑ The city council conducted a study on public transportation that was lengthy and that was detailed.
Ⓒ The city council conducted a lengthy, detailed study on public transportation.
Ⓓ The city council conducted a study on public transportation which was lengthy. The study was detailed.

9. Combine these short sentences to make a single sentence.

Advertisements are broadcast daily. Advertisements reach a wide audience.

Ⓐ Advertisements are broadcast daily and reach a wide audience.
Ⓑ Advertisements are broadcast daily , however, they reach a wide audience.
Ⓒ Advertisements are broadcast daily while they reach a wide audience.
Ⓓ Advertisements are broadcast daily, they reach a wide audience.

10. Combine these short sentences to make a single sentence.

The male horn-bill builds a nest for his mate. He guards her and the chicks from predators.

Ⓐ The male horn-bill builds a nest for his mate so he guards her and the chicks from predators.
Ⓑ The male horn-bill builds a nest for his mate where he guards her and the chicks from predators.
Ⓒ The male horn-bill builds a nest for his mate but he guards her and the chicks from predators.
Ⓓ The male horn-bill builds a nest for his mate, he guards her and the chicks from predators.

Chapter 5

Lesson 10: Develop And Strengthen Editing

1. **Consider grammar and punctuation to rewrite this passage. Insert periods in the right places.**

It was hard moving away from home I didn't have any friends in our new place I looked around at the kids in my class but I didn't see even one friendly face I didn't think I was going to like it here.

Ⓐ It was hard moving away from home I didn't have any friends in our new place. I looked around at the kids in my class but. I didn't see even one friendly face I didn't think I was going to like it here.

Ⓑ It was hard moving away from home. I didn't have any friends in our new place. I looked around at the kids in my new class, but I didn't see even one friendly face. I didn't think I was going to like it here.

Ⓒ it was hard moving away from home I didn't have. any friends in our new place? I looked around at the kids in my class. but I didn't see even one friendly face I didn't think I was going to like it here.

Ⓓ It was hard. Moving away from home. I didn't have any friends. in our new place I looked around at the kids in my class but. I didn't see even one friendly face I didn't think I was going to like it here.

2. **Consider grammar and punctuation to rewrite this passage. Insert quotation marks in the right places.**

Are these yours? Billy asked, as he held up my sunglasses. Yes, thank you! I said. I've been look-ing everywhere for those.

Ⓐ Are these yours? "Billy asked, as he held up my sunglasses." " Yes, thank you! I said." I've been looking everywhere for those.

Ⓑ "Are these yours? Billy asked, as he held up my sunglasses. Yes, thank you! I said. I've been looking everywhere for those."

Ⓒ Are these yours? Billy asked, "as he held up my sunglasses." Yes, thank you! I said. "I've been looking everywhere for those.

Ⓓ "Are these yours?" Billy asked, as he held up my sunglasses. "Yes, thank you!" I said."I've been looking everywhere for those."

3. **Consider grammar and punctuation to rewrite this passage. Insert commas in the right places.**

Last night for dinner we had green salad asparagus and spinach at the same meal. Don't you agree that is too many vegetables? But of course if we had pie ice cream and soda I don't think it would be too many sweets! Why do we have to have healthy food for breakfast lunch and dinner?

Ⓐ Last night for dinner ,we had green salad asparagus, and spinach at the same meal. Don't you agree that is too many vegetables? But, of course, if we had pie ice cream and soda, I don't think it would be too many sweets! Why do we have to have healthy food for breakfast lunch and dinner?

Ⓑ Last night for dinner we had green salad asparagus and spinach at the same meal. Don't you agree that is too many vegetables? But of course if we had pie ice cream and soda I don't think it would be too many sweets! Why do we have to have healthy food for breakfast, lunch, and dinner?

Ⓒ Last night for dinner, we had green salad, asparagus, and spinach at the same meal. Don't you agree that is too many vegetables? But, of course, if we had pie, ice cream, and soda, I don't think it would be too many sweets! Why do we have to have healthy food for breakfast, lunch, and dinner?

Ⓓ Last night for dinner we had green salad asparagus and spinach at the same meal. Don't you agree that is too many vegetables. But of course, if we had pie, ice cream, and soda I don't think it would be too many sweets! Why do we have to have healthy food for breakfast lunch and dinner?

4. **Consider grammar and punctuation to rewrite this passage.**

I asked my mother can we go to the beach she said didn't you notice that it's raining and cold I asked her if I could wear my raincoat, but she said we had to wait for another day.

Ⓐ "I asked my mother can we go to the beach she said didn't you notice that it's raining and cold I asked her if I could wear my raincoat, but she said we had to wait for another day."

Ⓑ I asked, my mother "can we go to the beach", she said, "didn't , you notice that it's raining, and cold! I asked her if I could wear my raincoat, but she said we had to wait for another day.

Ⓒ "I asked my mother can we go to the beach." she said didn't you notice that it's raining and cold. I asked her if I could wear my raincoat, but she said we had to wait for another day.

Ⓓ I asked my mother, "Can we go to the beach?" She said, "Didn't you notice that it's raining and cold?" I asked her if I could wear my raincoat, but she said we had to wait for another day.

5. **Consider grammar and punctuation to rewrite this passage. Insert apostrophes in all the contractions and the possessives in the right places.**

"Dont go out when its so cold and wet," said my mother. "Youll need your jacket and an umbrella. The sun isnt shining and the rain hasnt quit. Borrow your sisters jacket if you cant find yours."

Ⓐ "Dont go out when its so cold and wet," said my mother. "You'll need your jacket and an umbrella. The sun isnt shining and the rain hasnt quit. Borrow your sisters jacket if you cant find your's."

Ⓑ "Don't go out when it's so cold and wet," said my mother. "You'll need your jacket and an umbrella. The sun isn't shining, and the rain hasn't quit. Borrow your sister's jacket if you can't find yours."

Ⓒ "Dont go out when its so cold and wet," said my mother. "You'll need your jacket and an umbrella. The sun isnt shining and the rain hasnt quit. Borrow your sisters' jacket if you cant find yours."

Ⓓ "Don't go out when its so cold and wet," said my mother. "Youll need your jacket and an umbrella. The sun isnt shining and the rain hasnt quit. Borrow your sisters' jacket if you cant find your's."

6. **Your teacher has given a writing task. She wants the finished writing to be perfect in grammar. To ensure the quality of your writing which of the following would you do?**

Ⓐ Edit it.
Ⓑ Refer to a grammar book and make sure your grammar is correct.
Ⓒ Get it edited by an expert.
Ⓓ All of the above.

7. **You are asked to edit a fiction story that your friend has written. What is the most important thing for you to fix?**

Ⓐ His story idea. If it's not good you need to tell him to change it.
Ⓑ You need to change his style or voice if it's not good.
Ⓒ You need to check grammar, spelling and punctuation.
Ⓓ You just read it and give him your opinion.

8. **What is the last step in the process of writing?**

Ⓐ Drafting
Ⓑ Proofreading
Ⓒ Revising
Ⓓ Publishing

9. Choose a more interesting verb to replace the underlined word in the passage.

I went to the store. I looked everywhere for the perfect gift. I had carefully kept every penny I made that summer to get my mother a gift. And now I couldn't <u>see</u> anything that was good enough.

Ⓐ look at
Ⓑ locate
Ⓒ find
Ⓓ 'b' and 'c'

10. How many mistakes can you find in the writing given below:

One day, I help my mother clean up the backyard We put dry leaves in blue bags to recycle tham. We sawed some branch of a tree that was leaning againt the house. I felt good that day because i helped my Mother.

Ⓐ 5 mistakes.
Ⓑ 6 mistakes.
Ⓒ 4 mistakes.
Ⓓ no mistakes.

Answer Key and Detailed Explanations

Chapter 5: Composition

Lesson 1: Style Appropriate Task, Purpose, And Audience

Question No.	Answer	Detailed Explanations
1	A	Since this poster gives information, it is in the informational category.
2	B	The poster clearly states that it will take place in the amphitheater.
3	D	The poster gives all of the above information, so answer choice D is correct.
4	D	It is not clear exactly who the intended audience is for the poster, so we assume the audience is anyone who sees it.
5	B	If you selected b, you made a good choice. The writer is giving information, so the writing is informational or expository.
6	A	The main purpose of this passage is to tell a story, so narrative is the correct answer. This is not an account of someone's life (biography), or persuasive. Also, the purpose of the paragraph is not to give information but simply to entertain.
7	C	The best title would be answer choice C, "A Rainy Day." A is not correct because that's only one part of the story. B is not correct because it didn't turn out to be a bad day after all. D is not correct because it is too long of a title and sounds strange.
8	A	Answer choice A is correct. All of the descriptions and sights mentioned are outside of the train as he looked out the windows. Nowhere is inside the train mentioned and nowhere does the author try to persuade us to go on a train ride.
9	D	If it is in the middle of the school day, you can assume that the intended audience is a student.
10	D	Based on the part of the speech, it is clear that it is someone running for a position in student government at a school. The correct answer is D.

Lesson 2: Develop And Strengthen Planning

Question No.	Answer	Detailed Explanations
1	C	You might be able to find information at these places, but the absolute best choice would be the biography about the life of Louis Pasteur.
2	D	All of the above sources would give you good information about owls, so answer choice D is correct.
3	A	The first step is always to pick what you're going to write about. You can't even begin pre-writing until you've made that decision.
4	B	A rough draft is just that...a rough draft. It allows you to express your ideas without worrying about how they sound. You can fix that in revision.
5	D	It doesn't matter what type of writing you are doing, it is always best to get your ideas down on paper before you begin writing. You can make a list or do a graphic organizer to help you, but you always begin with ideas.
6	A	Good writing comes from personal experience. You should never copy someone else's work, and you definitely won't come up with any good ideas by not thinking about it.
7	D	In order to have a really great story, you need all of the above things.
8	D	Although writing is better when you do a rough draft, some writers dont have to write one. However, every good story has a beginning, middle and an end and descriptive details make a story much more interesting.
9	B	The main character is the lead character in the story. The character will be well developed, meaning you know the character well enough to make predictions about what he/she will do.
10	D	In order to have an interesting story, there has to be a plot (or a sequence of events.) These are sometimes good and sometimes bad, but without them there is no story.

Lesson 3: Transitions To Clarify

Question No.	Answer	Detailed Explanations
1	C	Answer choice C contains the only transition word that makes sense in this sentence. Answer choices A, B and D just don't work. They either don't make sense, or they change the meaning of the sentence.
2	B	Answer choices A and C are not correct because they are opposite transition words meaning "but". "Because" doesn't make sense. The answer choice that makes the most sense is B. "In fact" is adding to the information that it ended well. It's adding that it EVEN ended with those words.
3	C	Answer choice C is correct. Transition words can be at the beginning of a sentence or sentences, or they can be in the middle of two sentences that are being combined. Examples using the transition word "although" follow: Although Alley likes broccoli, she doesn't want to eat it every day. Alley likes broccoli although she doesn't want to eat it every day.
4	A	Answer choices B, C and D all have transition words that add information. Answer choice A is the only one that has an opposite transition word. That's the only one that effectively combines the two sentences.
5	C	For the blank numbered #1, you need a word that indicated that an opposite idea will be presented. "Consequently" means "so" and "In fact" adds additional information. "However" is an opposite word but it does not add meaning in the first sentence. The only one that indicates an opposite idea and gives the sentence meaning is answer choice C, "Although".
6	A	Answer choice B does not work because "in addition" is adding information. Answer choice C is an opposite word (which is what is needed), but "although" does not work in this sentence. Answer choice D is not correct because "in conclusion" does not make sense when it's not the last sentence of a paragraph. Answer choice A is correct because it is an opposite word that makes sense in the sentence.
7	C	In this blank, there is an idea being continued from the previous sentence. There is information being added, so answer choice C is correct. Eventually does not make sense in this sentence, and an opposite word is not needed. "Therefore" would be like using "so" in the blank, and that doesn't make sense either.

Question No.	Answer	Detailed Explanations
8	B	Answer choice B is the only one that can be used in the middle of the sentence with no punctuation. The other transitions will only work with proper punctuation. Otherwise, they are run-ons.
9	C	Answer choice C is correct because either "eventually" or "finally" sounds good to begin the last sentence of the paragraph.
10	B	All of the transition words have a purpose at different points in a paragraph or passage. "In conclusion" is the only one of the above that sounds like an ending. The others are used in the passage, but not as the last sentence.

Lesson 4: Vary Sentence Style

Question No.	Answer	Detailed Explanations
1	B	Answer choice A does not flow well, and neither does answer choice D. Answer choice C does not communicate the same thing as the original sentences. The correct answer is B because it is correct and sounds the best.
2	B	The only answer choice that contains sentences that are correctly combined is answer choice B. In the other sentences, the meaning has been slightly altered.
3	A	The answer choice that shows the cause/effect relationship between the two thoughts is answer A. The other choices do not communicate the same thing as the original sentences.
4	A	The witness refused to say anything and THAT'S why he/she was put in jail. The only answer choice that shows the correct cause/effect relationship is answer choice A.
5	C	The only answer that makes sense is answer choice C. The other answer choices use a word to connect the ideas that changes the meaning of the sentence.
6	A	The correctly written sentence is A. It correctly uses a conjunctive adverb (however). You have to put a semicolon before the conjunctive adverb and then a comma after a conjunctive adverb. It must be two complete sentences or this will not work. Answer choice B is not correct because there should be a comma before the "and" to make it a compound sentence. Answer choices C and D are not punctuated correctly. There should also not be any punctuation in answer choice C, and answer choice D is in the wrong order.
7	C	The answer choice containing the sentence in the correct order and punctuated correctly is answer choice C. The other sentences either do not make sense, or the wrong connector is used.
8	B	Answer choice A is not correct because there should be a comma before the "and" making a compound sentence. Answer choice B is correct because it is a correctly written and punctuated sentence. Answer choice C is not correct because it doesn't make sense. Answer choice D is not correct because you do not use "and" and "so" together as conjunctions.

Question No.	Answer	Detailed Explanations
9	D	Answer choice D is the correct answer because it's a correctly written compound sentence. Answer choice A is incorrect because it's a run-on. You can not put two sentences together with only a comma. Answer choice B is incorrect because therefore does not make sense in this sentence. C is incorrect because you cannot start the second sentence with so. Also, so does not make sense in this sentence.
10	D	Answer choices A and B are incorrect because "but" and "however" do not make sense in the sentence. Answer choice C is incorrect because there needs to be a comma before the "and" in order for it to be a correctly punctuated compound sentence. Answer choice D is correct because it is a correctly written and punctuated complex sentence.

Lesson 5: Introduce And Conclude The Topic

Question No.	Answer	Detailed Explanations
1	A	Answer choice A is correct because it is an effective introductory sentence and goes well with the rest of the paragraph. The other three answers either aren't true or do not effectively introduce the paragraph.
2	B	Because Ptolemy is introduced in the second sentence, his name would not be used in the first sentence. That eliminates answer choices A and C. Answer choice D would not be correct because you would not make a claim like that and then repeat yourself two sentences later. That leaves answer choice B, which broadly introduces the topic before the specifics are mentioned.
3	B	The correct answer is B because it's the best sentence to conclude the paragraph. The other three sentences are details and do not sound like concluding sentences.
4	A	Answer choice A is the only sentence that makes sense an an introduction. The paragraph is almost entirely about reading, so D doesn't make sense. B and C do not sound good if you read them with the rest of the paragraph.
5	D	Even though all of the sentences are about recycling, D has the best introduction. It tells the reader what he is going to read about, which is exactly what an introduction should do. The other answers are true, but do not introduce the topics.
6	D	Answer choice D is the only sentence that sounds like a conclusion and not just a supporting detail.
7		Possible answers include such things as: It is autumn. Autumn is a wonderful season. I like autumn,
8		Possible answers: It was a bad beginning. There's light at the end of the tunnel. Now, I call this a turnaround of sorts.
9		Possible answers: A good friend is forever. He is the best friend that I have had. I love my friend.
10		Possible answers. I now know that I misunderstood my dad. I have learned not to judge too quickly. Although I didn't always understand him, my dad is amazing.

Lesson 6: Introduce Headings And Graphics

Question No.	Answer	Detailed Explanations
1	D	Answer choice D is the most specific and complete title. Animals and Africa are too general. There are wild animals in places other than Africa, so the best title would be Africa's Wild Animals.
2	B	The pages about guarding yourself from diseases would be the place to look for information on how not to get sick.
3	A	According to the table of contents, there are 6 chapters in this book.
4	A	Chapter 3 is about what to eat to be healthy, so A is the answer.
5	A	The paragraph is about the central nervous system, so a scientific drawing of it would aid in our understanding of it.
6	D	B and C both contain appropriate headings, so answer choice D is correct.
7	B	There are 7 headings under the title.
8	D	Answer choice D is the only one that contains three of the headings.
9	C	There are only 4 subheadings under local transport, so answer choice C is correct.
10	D	They are under the subheading of Traditional means, so answer choice D is correct.

Lesson 7: Convey Ideas And Descriptive Details

Question No.	Answer	Detailed Explanations
1	B	Because the story mentions a gun and we see no evidence of comedy, that rules out A, and C. Fairy tales are very easy to recognize, and this is not one. The only reasonable answer is B, an action story.
2	C	It is obvious that this is not fiction, it is non-fiction. It is informational, but it's not about a person, so that means it's not A or D. That leaves C, an essay.
3	A	This is clearly not a fairy tale or a funny story, you can tell that by the mood that is created. The only possible answer is A.
4	C	This story is realistic fiction. It is set in modern day times and it is obviously fiction. It is definitely not science fiction, and it's definitely not mythology. A fairy tale would sound very different.
5	A	This is not a persuasive piece of writing; no one is trying to convince anyone of anything. Because this story does not sound funny or scary, mythology is definitely the only option.
6	D	This type of writing is far from realistic because some the things mentioned would never happen in real life. It's definitely not funny and there is nothing mysterious. Science fiction is the correct answer because that's when people have jetpacks and animals have lazer eyes.
7	C	There is nothing realistic, scary or science fiction about "in a kingdom far away" but that is the way most fairy tales begin. The answer is C.
8	C	Because there is a fox talking, we can immediately rule out realistic fiction. There really isn't anything funny happening in the story, and there are no elements of science fiction. The correct answer is a fable. It is a story that teaches a lesson.
9	D	There is nothing funny in the story, and all of the details point to trying to figure something out. That is evidence of a mystery, so the answer is D.
10	B	It is not a fable because there is no lesson presented, and this story is definitely not realistic. A biography is an account of someone's life. The only possible answer for this question is B, tall tale.

Lesson 8: Sensory Language Conveyed

Question No.	Answer	Detailed Explanations
1		Possible answers. a. The kitchen is filled with aromas that tingle my taste buds. b. Vegetables and fruits of many colors are a feast to the eyes. c. The clang of pots and pans and the sizzle on the stove are like music to my ears.
2		Possible answers a. To begin with, I love to see the players in their team colors. b. The cheering from the spectators is deafening to my ears. c. I am fascinated by the movements of the players.
3		Possible answers: I listen to the many sounds that send a shiver up my spine. I mistake the rustle of leaves for movements of beasts. The sounds of trees and animal calls make me sit still.
4		Possible answers: a. I took some time fastening my seat belt. b. I could see that some passengers looked a little scared. c. The whine of the engines told me we were about to taxi from the gate.
5		Possible answers: a. The sound that came from the surround-sound speakers was deafening. b. I could barely hear my phone that was ringing at the concert. c. It was a sight to see the crowd dancing away.
6		Possible answers: a. I was particularly attracted to the elephant. b. It was interesting to watch how different animals devoured food. c. I recorded some animal sounds and wondered what they were saying.
7		Possible answers. 1. The white snow was falling down as fast as a racing car. 2. The wet, cold flakes landed on the hard ground. 3. The snow piled up higher than the windows.
8		Possible answers: a. However, what followed didn't seem that easy. b. The climb on to the horse was itself quite difficult. c. The reins did not feel all that comfortable.

Question No.	Answer	Detailed Explanations
9		Possible answers. 1. The fireman pulled up his heavy fire resistant suit that weighed twenty extra pounds. 2. Water hissed out of the hydrant at the corner of the street. 3. The smell of burning wood overwhelmed the people.
10		Possible answers. 1. The room was filled with old broken boxes. 2. There were spider webs hanging from the ceiling. 3. The musty smell flew right up your noise when you opened the heavy door.

Lesson 9: Develop And Strengthen Revising

Question No.	Answer	Detailed Explanations
1	A	The reason for revision is to find and correct mistakes. That is the only answer that makes sense.
2	A	The sentence is not correct as it is because it is a run-on. Answer choices B and C are not correct because the commas are in the wrong place. Answer choice A is correct because it sounds much better for it to be two sentences.
3	B	Answer choices A, C, and D all have commas in the wrong places. The only correctly written and punctuated sentence is B.
4	C	Answer choices A,B, and D have commas that are not needed. There are not two complete sentences on either side of the "and", so a comma before the "and" is not needed. Also an "a" is needed before the word "gun". That is why answer choice C is correct.
5	C	"Romans" is the name of people from the country of Rome, so it is a proper noun and should be capitalized. That is why C is the correct answer.
6	D	Answer choice D is correct. There needs to be a comma between the city and the state, and also there needs to be a comma before the "and" because this is a compound sentence (two sentences joined together by a comma and a conjunction.)
7	D	The main problem is that the word "Oscar" should be capitalized because it is a proper noun. Answers A and B have commas that are not needed. Answer choice C is missing "the" before "Oscar." That is why answer choice D is correct.
8	C	The most well-written sentence is answer choice C. The other three answer choices don't sound nearly as good.
9	A	Answer choice D is not correct because you can 't put two sentences together with only a comma. Answer choices B and C are not correct because "however" and "while" do not make sense in the sentence. Answer choice A is correct because it is a correctly written simple sentence. There does not need to be a comma before "and" because there are not two complete sentences on each side of the "and." If there had been a complete sentence after the "and", then a comma before the "and" would be needed.
10	B	Answer choice D is not correct because you can not put two sentences together with only a comma. Answer choices A and C are not correct because they do not use the correct words to connect the two sentences. The correct answer is B because it is a correctly written sentence that uses the correct transition word.

Lesson 10: Develop And Strengthen Editing

Question No.	Answer	Detailed Explanations
1	B	Answer choice B is the only one that has correctly punctuated sentences. The other three answer choices have periods and other punctuation in the wrong places.
2	D	The sentence that has all of the quotation marks, commas and periods correct is answer choice D.
3	C	The only sentence that has all of the commas and other punctuation marks correct is answer choice C.
4	D	The only sentence with correctly written dialogue is answer choice D.
5	B	Answer choice B is the only answer with correctly placed punctuation. There are many contractions that needed apostrophes.
6	D	You might do all of these things if you were wanting something to be perfect before you turn it in, so answer choice D is correct.
7	C	Editing is checking grammar, spelling and punctuation, so answer choice C is correct.
8	D	The very last step in the writing process is publishing. The writing process is as follows: Brainstorming, Prewiting, Drafting, Revision and Editing, and then Publishing.
9	D	"Find" and "Locate" are both good answers, so answer choice D is correct.
10	B	The corrected version of the passage: One day, I help**ed** my mother clean up the backyard**.** We put dry leaves in blue bags to recycle **them**. We sawed some branch**es** of a tree that was leaning again**st** the house. I felt good that day because **I** helped my **mother**.

Chapter 6

Inquiry and Research

Chapter 6

Lesson 1: Gather Information From Multiple Sources

Read the passage and answer the following questions.

Philadelphia is a huge city with several districts containing sightseeing, restaurants, and nightlife. Philadelphia, located in southeastern Pennsylvania, on the southern fringe of the mid-Atlantic region, is the fourth-largest urban area in the United States and the country's fifth-largest city. Often referred to as "Philly," the official city boundaries are actually quite large. What started as a much smaller city began annexing the surrounding districts and suburbs in the mid-19th century, and Philadelphia the city is now coterminous with Philadelphia the county. Altogether, Philadelphia's metropolitan area encompasses a total of twelve counties in Pennsylvania, New Jersey, and Delaware.

1. **Complete the sentence by gathering relevant information from the passage.**

   Philadelphia was a small city before, but _____.

   Ⓐ has grown considerably after annexing surrounding areas.
   Ⓑ has now been annexed to its nearest district.
   Ⓒ is now a part of a nearby suburb.
   Ⓓ has now been annexed to its nearby county.

2. **Complete the sentence by gathering relevant information from the passage.**

   Philadelphia is located _____.

   Ⓐ in the northern fringe of the mid-Atlantic region
   Ⓑ in southeastern Pennsylvania
   Ⓒ on the southern fringe of Pennsylvania
   Ⓓ in the suburbs of New Jersey

3. **Choose the correct sentence by gathering relevant information from the passage.**

   Ⓐ Philadelphia is the fourth largest city in the United States.
   Ⓑ There are five cities that are bigger than Philadelphia.
   Ⓒ There are four cities that are bigger than Philadelphia.
   Ⓓ Philadelphia is the largest city in the United States.

4. **Select the correct choice by gathering relevant information from the passage.**

   Ⓐ Philadelphia is located on the southern fringe of the mid-Atlantic region.
   Ⓑ Philadelphia is located in southeastern Pennsylvania.
   Ⓒ Philadelphia is the fourth-largest urban area in the United States.
   Ⓓ All the above.

5. Select the correct choice by gathering relevant information from the passage.

Ⓐ Winters in Philadelphia are cold and snowy.
Ⓑ Summers in Philadelphia are hot and humid.
Ⓒ Both 'A' and 'B' are true according to the paragraph
Ⓓ Both 'A' and 'B' are not true according to the paragraph

Read the passage and answer the following questions.

Philadelphia has a humid continental climate with four distinct seasons. Winters are cold and often snowy, with temperatures usually hovering around 32°F (0°C) during the colder months. The average annual snowfall is 24 inches (59 cm) which is spread out mainly from December to March. The area is sometimes hit by devastating blizzards that can dump up to half that total or even more on the city in one day, such as in 1996 when a single storm dumped 30.7 inches (78 cm) of snow on the city in just a couple days.

Spring and fall are rather pleasant, with temperatures in the 60s and 70s F (15°C-25°C). Summers are hot and humid, and conditions can get quite unpleasant when the air temperature is near 90°F (32°C) and humidity is high.

6. Complete the sentence by gathering relevant information from the passage.

The most pleasant seasons in Philadelphia are_____.

Ⓐ summer
Ⓑ winter
Ⓒ fall
Ⓓ spring and fall

7. Complete the sentence by gathering relevant information from the passage.

The most unpleasant time in Philadelphia is _____.

Ⓐ when humidity and temperature are high
Ⓑ when temperature is in the 60s and 70s F range
Ⓒ when the temperature is usually hovering around 32°F (0°C)
Ⓓ Both 'A' and 'C'

Read the passage and answer the following questions.

New York is the most populated city in the United States of America and the center of the New York Metropolitan area. The city is referred to as New York City or The City of New York , so as not to confuse it with the State of New York, of which it is a part. New York significantly impacts commerce, finance, media, art, fashion, research, technology, education, and entertainment. It is also the home of the United Nations Headquarters and is an important center for international diplomacy. New York consists of five boroughs - The Bronx, Brooklyn, Manhattan, Queens, and Staten Island. In 2011, the population reached 8,244,910. New York is the most densely populated major city in the United States. As many as 800 languages are spoken in New York, making it the most linguistically diverse city in the world.

8. **Complete the sentence by gathering relevant information from the passage.**

   There are _____ boroughs in New York.

   Ⓐ Five
   Ⓑ Six
   Ⓒ One
   Ⓓ Four

9. **Complete the sentence by gathering relevant information from the passage.**

   New York City significantly impacts _____.

   Ⓐ Commerce, finance, art, farming
   Ⓑ Media, finance, gardening, entertainment
   Ⓒ Media, art, fashion, research
   Ⓓ Technology, education, fashion, recycling

10. **Complete the sentence by gathering relevant information from the passage.**

   _____ are a few of the names of the boroughs in New York City.

   Ⓐ The Bronx
   Ⓑ Brooklyn
   Ⓒ Manhattan
   Ⓓ All of the above

Chapter 6

Lesson 2: Information That Is Quoted And Paraphrased

When we go about paraphrasing a passage, we do the following:

1. Go through the passage carefully.
2. State the ideas in our own words.
3. We edit or clarify some ideas but do not change the meaning.
4. If we borrow phrases directly, we put them in quotation marks.
5. _____.

1. **Choose the last step to paraphrasing from the given choices.**

   Ⓐ We give out our own ideas in the end.
   Ⓑ We can change meanings if we want to.
   Ⓒ We check the paraphrase against the original for similar meaning
   Ⓓ We rewrite the passage in quotes.

2. **A paraphrase is a _____.**

   Ⓐ a poem written in your own words
   Ⓑ a summary of a piece of writing in your own words
   Ⓒ an edited version of a written piece of work
   Ⓓ a copy of any written work

Read the following lines.

Cleopatra ruled Egypt more than 2000 years ago. Much is known about the powerful queen. But a mystery still remains:
Where was she buried?

3. **Choose the best paraphrased version.**

   Ⓐ Where was Cleopatra buried? Much is known about the powerful queen. But a mystery still remains. Cleopatra ruled Egypt more than 2000years ago.
   Ⓑ Where was Cleopatra buried? The mystery still remains. Cleopatra ruled Egypt more than 2000years ago. Much is known about the powerful queen.
   Ⓒ "Cleopatra ruled Egypt more than 2000years ago. Much is known about the powerful queen. But a mystery still remains:
   Where was she buried?"
   Ⓓ The powerful queen Cleopatra ruled Egypt more than 2000 years ago. We know a lot about this queen, but where she is buried still remains a mystery.

Read the following lines.

People in Asia and Africa were busy gazing at the skies on Wednesday. They were looking at the partial solar eclipse. They were wearing dark glasses to protect their eyes from being damaged. The eclipse doesn't occur everyday.

4.   Choose the best paraphrased version.

Ⓐ People in Asia and Africa spent their time sky gazing on Wednesday. They were looking at the partial eclipse of the sun. Since looking directly at the Sun would damage their eyes, they were wearing dark glasses. The eclipse is a rare sight, and they did not want to miss it.

Ⓑ The Solar eclipse doesn't occur everyday. People in Asia and Africa were busy gazing at the skies on Wednesday. They were looking at the partial solar eclipse. They were wearing dark glasses to protect their eyes from being damaged.

Ⓒ "People in Asia and Africa were busy gazing at the skies on Wednesday. They were looking at the partial solar eclipse. They were wearing dark glasses to protect their eyes from being damaged. The eclipse doesn't occur everyday."

Ⓓ People in Asia and Africa were busy gazing at the skies on Wednesday. They were trying to look at the partial solar eclipse, which was rare indeed. Why were they wearing dark glasses? They were wearing dark glasses to protect their eyes from being damaged. What causes the damage? Seeing the Sun directly does. Does the eclipse occur everyday? The eclipse doesn't occur everyday.

Read the following lines.

Africa's evergreen forests are alive with millions of plants and animals, but the large area of this forest land is slowly dwindling. Land is being cleared for making cities, and trees are cut for wood and paper.

5. **Choose the best paraphrased version.**

   Ⓐ "Africa's evergreen forests are alive with millions of plants and animals. But the large area of this forest land is slowly dwindling. Land is being cleared for making cities and trees are cut for wood and paper."

   Ⓑ Africa's evergreen forests are alive with millions of plants and animals. But the large area of this forest land is slowly dwindling and land is being cleared for making cities and trees are cut for wood and paper.

   Ⓒ Africa's evergreen forests are filled with many many varieties of plants and animals, but the large forests are slowly shrinking in size. This is due to forest land being cleaned up to make cities. The number of trees are reducing too. They are being cut for wood and making paper.

   Ⓓ 1. Africa's evergreen forests are alive with millions of plants and animals.
      2. But the large area of this forest land is slowly dwindling.
      3. Land is being cleared for making cities and trees are cut for wood and paper.

The king is dead. There are many other ways of putting across this statement.

6. **Choose the sentence that conveys the meaning of this sentence in an inappropriate and crude manner.**

   Ⓐ The king is no more.
   Ⓑ The king breathed his last.
   Ⓒ The king has expired.
   Ⓓ The king kicked his bucket.

The time to repair the roof is when the sun is shining. John F. Kennedy

7. **Write the above statement in quotes:** _____.

   Ⓐ President Kennedy said, "The time to repair the roof is when the sun is shining".
   Ⓑ President Kennedy said that the time to repair the roof is when the sun is shining.
   Ⓒ "President Kennedy said, The time to repair the roof is when the sun is shining".
   Ⓓ President Kennedy said, The time to repair the roof is when the sun is shining.

President Kennedy tells us not to pray for easy lives, but tells us to pray to be stronger men.

8. **Write the above statement in quotes:** _____.

Ⓐ President Kennedy told the Americans, "Do not pray for easy lives. Pray to be stronger men".

Ⓑ "President Kennedy told the Americans, Do not pray for easy lives. Pray to be stronger men."

Ⓒ President Kennedy told the Americans, that Do not pray for easy lives. Pray to be stronger men.

Ⓓ President Kennedy told, "Americans, "Do not pray for easy lives. Pray to be stronger men".

Roger Federer, born on August 8, 1981, is a Swiss professional tennis player who held the ATP no. 1 position for a record 237 consecutive weeks. Federer has won a record 16 Grand Slam singles titles. There have been few tennis players who have been as successful.

9. **Choose the best paraphrased version.**

Ⓐ Roger Federer was born on August 8, 1981. He is a Swiss professional tennis player. He has held the ATP no. 1 position for a record 237 consecutive weeks. Federer has won a record 16 Grand Slam singles titles. There have been many tennis players who have been as successful.

Ⓑ Roger Federer, a Swiss professional tennis player, born on August 18, 1981, has undoubtedly been one of the most successful tennis players. He has held the ATP no 1 position for a record 237 consecutive weeks. In addition to this, he has also won a record number of 16 Grand Slam singles titles.

Ⓒ Roger Federer was born on August 8, 1981. He is a Swiss professional tennis player. He has held the ATP no. 1 position. He has held that position for a record 237 consecutive weeks. He has won 16 Grand Slam singles titles. He has won a record. He is one of the few tennis players who have also been successful.

Ⓓ Roger Federer, born on August 8, 1981 and a Swiss professional tennis player held the ATP no. 1 position for 237 consecutive weeks. That is a record indeed. Federer has won 16 Grand Slam singles titles. That's another record indeed. There have been few tennis players who have been as successful, and Roger if one of them.

Federer himself also credits the range of sports he played as a child—he played badminton and basketball along with tennis—for his hand-eye coordination. "I was always very much more interested if a ball was involved," he says. Most tennis prodigies, by contrast, play tennis to the exclusion of all other sports.

10. Select the choice that best paraphrases the above sentence.

Ⓐ Federer himself credits the range of sports he played as a child. He also played badminton and basketball for his hand-eye coordination. "I was always very much more interested if a ball was involved," he says. Most tennis prodigies play only tennis. They usually do not play the other sports.

Ⓑ "Federer himself also credits the range of sports he played as a child—he also played badminton and basketball—for his hand-eye coordination. "I was always very much more interested if a ball was involved," he says. Most tennis prodigies, by contrast, play tennis to the exclusion of all other sports."

Ⓒ Federer himself also gives credits to the range of sports he played as a child. He has also played badminton and basketball. He has played badminton and basketball for his hand-eye coordination. He says that he was always very much more interested if a ball was involved. Most tennis prodigies, by contrast, to Roger Federer play tennis. They try to the exclude all other sports.

Ⓓ "Federer himself also gives credit to the range of sports he played as a child—he also played badminton and basketball—for his hand-eye coordination. "I was always very much more interested if a ball was involved,". Most tennis prodigies play only tennis to the exclusion of all other sports."

Chapter 6

Lesson 3: Credible Sources

1. **Which of the following choices correctly defines "plagiarism" ?**

   Ⓐ Plagiarism is the act of presenting someone else's work as your own.
   Ⓑ Plagiarism is theft of someone else's ideas.
   Ⓒ Plagiarism is stealing an author's exact words and failing to use quotation marks or to cite the author.
   Ⓓ All the above statements.

2. **When you have taken information from a book for use in your publication, it is necessary to give details from where you have taken the information.**

   Those details should include: _____

   Ⓐ the name of the author
   Ⓑ the title of the book
   Ⓒ the publisher's name and date of publication
   Ⓓ The author's name, title of the book, date published, name of publisher and city of publication

3. **While citing resources, it is recommended that titles of books that you have taken information from, be in_____ .**

   Ⓐ in bold
   Ⓑ in italics
   Ⓒ in brackets /parentheses
   Ⓓ highlighted in red

4. **Choose the correct way to cite this below information.**

   The book called "America's Very Own Ghosts" is written by Daniel Cohen. Let's say you have used parts of this book for your writing. The book was published by Doubleday in 1985.

   Ⓐ NewYork: Doubleday, 1985. Daniel Cohen America's Very Own Ghosts.
   Ⓑ Daniel Cohen. America's very own ghosts, 1985, Doubleday
   Ⓒ Cohen, Daniel. America's Very Own Ghosts. NewYork: Doubleday, 1985.
   Ⓓ America's very own ghosts by Daniel Cohen. Doubleday 1985

5. What's the correct way to cite this below resource.

Lets say you have used some passages from Ernest Hemingway's "Green Hills of Africa."

Ⓐ *Green Hills of Africa by Hemingway Ernest. 1935 edition, Scribners in NewYork*

Ⓑ *Green Hills of Africa by Ernest hemingway*
New York: Scribners, 1935.

Ⓒ Ernest Hemingway
Green Hills of Africa.
New York: Scribners, 1935.

Ⓓ Hemingway, Ernest. *Green Hills of Africa.* New York: Scribners, 1935.

You did an interview with your school principal, Christie Whitman, for your school magazine.

6. Select from the choices below the best way to cite this information.

Ⓐ Whitman, Christie. Personal interview. 20 Nov. 2009
Ⓑ Personal Interview conducted with Christie Whitman by me on 20 nov, 2009
Ⓒ Christie Whitman Interview
Ⓓ Personal interview with Christie Whitman

7. If you have used an article from the internet, then you need to cite the _____.

Ⓐ full http address enclosed in angle brackets
Ⓑ only the author and the name of the article
Ⓒ the year and name of the article
Ⓓ the author of the article, name of the article, date, publishing information, and the url (internet address.)

You have been doing a project on Mark Twain's works. You have quoted parts of his work "The Adventures of Huckleberry Finn".

8. Where else would you look for good information about this book?

Ⓐ A biography of the author, Mark Twain
Ⓑ A book of professionally written essays about the book.
Ⓒ An autobiography by Mark Twain.
Ⓓ A picture book version of the book.

9. While quoting a resource from a novel, make sure you mention _____.

Ⓐ the website
Ⓑ the title, author, publisher's name, place where published and year published.
Ⓒ the page number of the information
Ⓓ the author name, the year he/she was born and date of birth

10. The act of presenting someone else's work as your own is called _____.

Ⓐ copyright
Ⓑ plagiarism
Ⓒ imagination
Ⓓ poetry

Answer Key and
Detailed Explanations

Chapter 6: Inquiry and Research

Lesson 1: Gather Information From Multiple Sources

Question No.	Answer	Detailed Explanations
1	A	Answer choice A is the only true statement among the four answer choices.
2	B	The paragraph specifically says that Philly is located in southeastern Pennsylvania, so the correct answer is B.
3	C	Since Philadelphia is the 5th largest city, you know that there are four cities larger. That is why C is the correct answer.
4	D	The paragraphs include all of the information listed above, so answer choice D is correct.
5	D	The paragraphs do not mention the weather at all; therefore, according to the paragraph these statements are not true.
6	D	According to the passage above, answer choice D is correct.
7	D	According to the passage above, the answer is A and C.
8	A	According to the passage, there are five.
9	C	According to the passage, the correct answer is C. That is the only answer choice where all of the things were mentioned in the paragraph as things that New York impacts.
10	D	All of the above are mentioned as one of the five boroughs in the City of New York.

Lesson 2: Information That Is Quoted And Paraphrased

Question No.	Answer	Detailed Explanations
1	C	The paraphrase should contain the same information as the original; it will just be in different words. You cannot change the meaning and you do not use quotes when paraphrasing. You also do not give your own ideas when you are paraphrasing something. You simply stick to the facts.
2	B	Paraphrasing is when you take a passage or paragraph and you put it into your own words, so answer choice B is correct.
3	D	Answer choices A, B, and C are just the same words rearranged. The only one that is a true paraphrase is answer choice D.
4	A	Answer choices B and C do not change the words enough. Answer choice D contains roughly worded questions and answers. The correct answer is A because it is the only true paraphrase.
5	C	Answers A, B and D are all almost the same words as the original. The only one that is truly a paraphrase is answer choice C.
6	D	The most insensitive way of putting that the king died is answer choice D.
7	A	The answer choice that contains the quote correctly written and punctuated is answer choice A. You only put in quotation marks what the person actually says out loud.
8	A	The answer choice with the correctly written quotation is answer choice A. You only put in quotation marks what the person actually says.
9	B	The answer choice that contains the most complete and best worded paraphrase is answer B. A paraphrase should relay the exact same information but should not be in the same words as the original.
10	A	The quotes should not be around paraphrases, so that eliminates answer choices B and D. Answer choice C is almost exactly the same as the original. The only true paraphrase is answer choice A.

Lesson 3: Credible Sources

Question No.	Answer	Detailed Explanations
1	D	All of the answer choices correctly define plagiarism, so answer choice D is correct.
2	D	When citing a source, you should list as much information as you can. The point is that someone should be able to easily find the exact place your information was originally found.
3	B	Titles of books should either be underlines or in italics when they are listed.
4	C	It makes sense to list the title and Author before the publishing city, so answer choice A cannot be correct. Answer choices B and D have major errors such as the words of the title not being capitalized. That's why answer choice C is correct.
5	D	The author and title will always be listed first when citing sources. For that reason, answer choice D is correct.
6	A	The correct way to cite the source is A. You always give as much information as you have.
7	D	You need to include as much information as possible when you cite sources. For this reason, answer choice D is correct.
8	B	Answer choice B contains the best answer. You would not need a book about Mark Twain to find out information about his books. It would be better to read essays written about the book and cite the sources correctly.
9	B	When citing a novel, you want to give enough information that someone would be able to find it again. The information you would need is listed in answer choice B. You would not need things such as the year the author is born; that is unnecessary information that would not help you find the book.
10	B	Answer choice B is correct because that is the technical definition of plagiarism.

STAAR FAQs

What will STAAR ELA Assessment Look Like?

In many ways, the STAAR assessments will be unlike anything many students have ever seen. The tests will be conducted either as pencil & paper test or as an online assessment. These assessments require students to complete tasks that assess a deeper understanding of the Texas Essential Knowledge and Skills (TEKS).

The STAAR assessments are designed so that students can complete the 3rd–5th grade assessments in two hours and the 6th–8th grade assessments in three hours. If needed, students can take up to four hours to complete their assessment. The testing time begins after all directions are read to the students. Students may be allowed to take breaks during testing, potentially including breaks for snacks or meals.

How is this Lumos tedBook aligned to STAAR Guidelines?

The practice tests provided in the Lumos Program were created to reflect the depth and rigor of the State of Texas Assessment of Academic Readiness based on the information published by the test administrator. However, the content and format of the State of Texas Assessment of Academic Readiness that is officially administered to the students could be different compared to these practice tests.

What Question types are included in the Online STAAR?

The question types that you will encounter on the Texas STAAR assessments are:

In ELA:
Multiple Choice Single Answer
Constructed Response (only in Writing tests for Grade 4 and Grade 7)

In Math:
Multiple Choice Single Answer
Grid in

For more information on 2021-22 Assessment year, visit
http://www.lumoslearning.com/a/staar-2021-faqs OR
Scan the **QR Code**

What does the STAAR Test Practice book provide?

Inside this book, you will find practice sections aligned to each TEKS. Students will have the ability to review questions on each standard, one section at a time, in the order presented, or they can choose to study the sections where they need the most practice.

In addition to the practice sections, you will have access to two full-length practice tests online. Completing these tests will help students master the different areas that are included in newly aligned STAAR tests and practice test taking skills. The results will help the students and educators get insights into students' strengths and weaknesses in specific content areas. These insights could be used to help students strengthen their skills in difficult topics and to improve speed and accuracy while taking the test.

Because the STAAR assessment includes questions covering various TEKS standards, it is necessary for students to be able to regularly practice these questions. The Lumos online StepUp program provides practice tests that mimic the state assessments.

Why Practice with Repeated Reading Passages?

Throughout the Lumos Learning Common Core Practice workbooks, students and educators will notice many passages repeat. This is done intentionally. The goal of these workbooks is to help students practice skills necessary to be successful in class and on standardized tests. One of the most critical components to that success is the ability to read and comprehend passages. To that end, reading fluency must be strengthened. According to Hasbrouck and Tindal (2006), "Helping our students become fluent readers is absolutely critical for proficient and motivated reading" (p. 642). And, Nichols et al. indicate, (2009), "fluency is a gateway to comprehension that enables students to move from being word decoders to passage comprehenders" (p. 11).

Lumos Learning recognizes there is no one-size-fits-all approach to build fluency in readers; however, the repeated reading of passages, where students read the same passages at least two or more times, is one of the most widely recognized strategies to improve fluency (Nichols et al., 2009). Repeated reading allows students the opportunity to read passages with familiar words several times until the passage becomes familiar and they no longer have to decode word by word. As students reread, the decoding barrier falls away allowing for an increase in reading comprehension.

The goal of the Lumos Learning workbooks is to increase student achievement and preparation for any standardized test. Using some passages multiple times in a book offers struggling readers an opportunity to do just that.

References
Hasbrouck, J., and Tindal, G. (2006). Oral reading fluency norms: A valuable assessment tool for reading teachers. Reading Teacher, 59(7), 636644. doi:10.1598/RT.59.7.3.
Nichols, W., Rupley, W., and Rasinski, T. (2009). Fluency in learning to read for meaning: going beyond repeated readings. Literacy Research & Instruction, 48(1). doi:10.1080/19388070802161906.

Discover Engaging and Relevant Learning Resources

Lumos EdSearch is a safe search engine specifically designed for teachers and students. Using EdSearch, you can easily find thousands of standards-aligned learning resources such as questions, videos, lessons, worksheets, and apps. Teachers can use EdSearch to create custom resource kits to perfectly match their lesson objective and assign them to one or more students in their classroom.

To access the EdSearch tool, use the search box after you log into Lumos StepUp or use the link provided below.

http://www.lumoslearning.com/a/edsearchb	

The Lumos Standards Coherence map provides information about previous level, next level and related standards. It helps educators and students visually explore learning standards. It's an effective tool to help students progress through the learning objectives. Teachers can use this tool to develop their own pacing charts and lesson plans. Educators can also use the coherence map to get deep insights into why a student is struggling in a specific learning objective.

Teachers can access the Coherence maps after logging into the StepUp Teacher Portal or use the link provided below.

http://www.lumoslearning.com/a/coherence-map	

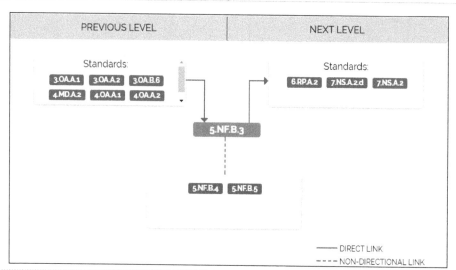

What if I buy more than one Lumos Study Program?

Step 1

Visit the URL and login to your account.
http://www.lumoslearning.com

Step 2

Click on 'My tedBooks' under the "Account" tab.
Place the Book Access Code and submit.

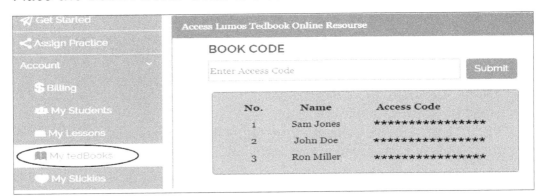

Step 3

To add the new book for a registered student, choose the
Existing Student button and select the student and submit.

To add the new book for a new student, choose the Add New student
button and complete the student registration.

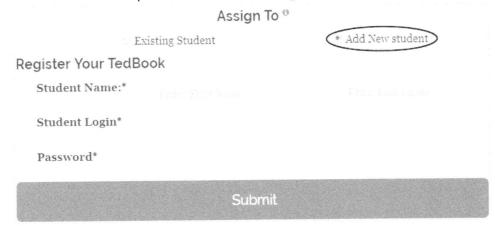

Lumos StepUp® Mobile App FAQ For Students

What is the Lumos StepUp® App?

It is a FREE application you can download onto your Android Smartphones, tablets, iPhones, and iPads.

What are the Benefits of the StepUp® App?

This mobile application gives convenient access to Practice Tests, Common Core State Standards, Online Workbooks, and learning resources through your Smartphone and tablet computers.
- Eleven Technology enhanced question types in both MATH and ELA
- Sample questions for Arithmetic drills
- Standard specific sample questions
- Instant access to the Common Core State Standards
- Jokes and cartoons to make learning fun!

Do I Need the StepUp® App to Access Online Workbooks?

No, you can access Lumos StepUp® Online Workbooks through a personal computer. The StepUp® app simply enhances your learning experience and allows you to conveniently access StepUp® Online Workbooks and additional resources through your smartphone or tablet.

How can I Download the App?

Visit **lumoslearning.com/a/stepup-app** using your Smartphone or tablet and follow the instructions to download the app.

QR Code
for Smartphone
Or Tablet Users

Lumos StepUp® Mobile App FAQ For Parents and Teachers

What is the Lumos StepUp® App?

It is a free app that teachers can use to easily access real-time student activity information as well as assign learning resources to students. Parents can also use it to easily access school-related information such as homework assigned by teachers and PTA meetings. It can be downloaded onto smartphones and tablets from popular App Stores.

What are the Benefits of the Lumos StepUp® App?

It provides convenient access to

- Standards aligned learning resources for your students
- An easy to use Dashboard
- Student progress reports
- Active and inactive students in your classroom
- Professional development information
- Educational Blogs

How can I Download the App?

Visit **lumoslearning.com/a/stepup-app** using your Smartphone or tablet and follow the instructions to download the app.

**QR Code
for Smartphone
Or Tablet Users**

Progress Chart

Standard	Lesson	Page No.	Practice		Mastered	Re-practice /Reteach
TEKS			Date	Score		
ELAR 6.1	Speaking & Listening	11				
ELAR 6.2.A	Use Clues To Determine Multiple-meaning Words	12				
ELAR 6.2.A	Interpret Figures Of Speech	16				
ELAR 6.2.B	Use Context Clue To Determine Word Meaning	19				
ELAR 6.2.C	Use Common Roots And Affixes	22				
ELAR 6.2.C	Determine The Meaning Of A Word	24				
ELAR 6.6.B	Use Relationships To Better Understand Words	27				
ELAR 6.6.H	Maintain Consistency In Style And Tone	30				
ELAR 6.8.D.ii	Consult Reference Materials	33				
ELAR 6.9.E	Recognize Variations In English	35				
ELAR 6.9.G	Distinguish Between Word Associations And Definitions	38				
ELAR 6.10.C	Vary Sentence	40				
ELAR 6.10.C.i	Correct Subject-verb Agreement	43				
ELAR 6.10.C.iii	Correct Use Of Adjectives And Adverbs	46				
ELAR 6.10.C.v	Recognize Pronouns	49				
ELAR 6.10.C.v	Recognize And Correct Vague Pronouns	52				
ELAR 6.10.C.vii	Recognize And Correct Shifts In Pronoun Number And Person	55				
ELAR 6.10.C.vii	Demonstrate Command Of Capitalization	58				
ELAR 6.10.C.viii	Demonstrate Command Of Punctuation	61				
ELAR 6.10.C.ix	Correct Spelling	64				
ELAR 6.10.D	Use Grade Appropriate Words	67				
ELAR 6.2.A	Determine Technical Meanings	93				
ELAR 6.2.B	Connotative Words And Phrases	95				
ELAR 6.2.B	Meaning Of Words And Phrases	99				
ELAR 6.5.E	Development Of Ideas	103				

Standard	Lesson	Page No.	Practice		Mastered	Re-practice /Reteach
TEKS			Date	Score		
ELAR 6.5.E	Analyze How People, Events, Or Ideas Are Presented In Text	107				
ELAR 6.5.G	Central Idea Of The Text	111				
ELAR 6.6.D	Summary Of Text	114				
ELAR 6.6.I	Evaluating Arguments In Text	118				
ELAR 6.7.B	Characters Responses And Changes	122				
ELAR 6.7.C	Develop Setting	126				
ELAR 6.8.B	Analysis Of Key Events And Ideas	130				
ELAR 6.8.B	Conclusions Drawn From The Text	135				
ELAR 6.8.E	Structure Of Text	139				
ELAR 6.8.E.ii	Cite Textual Evidence	143				
ELAR 6.9.A	Determine Author's Point Of View	147				
ELAR 6.9.B	Author's Purpose In A Text	151				
ELAR 6.9.D	Figurative Words And Phrases	155				
ELAR 6.9	Comparing Author's Writing To Another	179				
ELAR 6.9.B	Compare/contrast One Author's Presentation With Another	182				
ELAR 6.10.A	Style Appropriate Task, Purpose, And Audience	189				
ELAR 6.10.A	Develop And Strengthen Planning	193				
ELAR 6.10.B	Transitions To Clarify	196				
ELAR 6.10.B	Vary Sentence Style	200				
ELAR 6.10.B.i	Introduce And Conclude The Topic	203				
ELAR 6.10.B.i	Introduce Headings And Graphics	207				
ELAR 6.10.B.ii	Convey Ideas And Descriptive Details	213				
ELAR 6.10.C	Sensory Language Conveyed	217				
ELAR 6.12.B	Develop And Strengthen Revising	221				
ELAR 6.12.B	Develop And Strengthen Editing	224				
ELAR 6.12.D	Gather Information From Multiple Sources	243				
ELAR 6.12.E	Information That Is Quoted And Paraphrased	246				
ELAR 6.12.H.i	Credible Sources	251				

Available

- At Leading book stores
- Online www.LumosLearning.com

CPSIA information can be obtained
at www.ICGtesting.com
Printed in the USA
LVHW010159050522
717841LV00063B/3435